Raising Horses

The Ultimate Guide To Horse Breeding, Training And Care

Contents

Introduction

The horse is one of the most versatile and beautiful creatures in the animal kingdom. It has been a faithful companion of man for centuries and will surely continue to be. This majestic animal serves so many important purposes, and today, it is not uncommon to find people raising them.

If you have even the slightest interest of raising or breeding one, this book is definitely for you. Everything you need to know about horses, training them, understanding their behavior, caring, and creating a lifelong relationship with them is all written here.

Whatever reason you may have for wanting to be a horse owner, you will find this guide to be the perfect book to assist you on your journey.

Pick it up, read it, and share it with other horse friends!

Chapter One: Why Raise Horses?

The relationship between horses and men began over 3,000 years ago. Surprising, right? The domestication of horses dates to 3,500BC. Horses have been such versatile creatures that raising them provides a ton of benefits – companionship being one of such. It is interesting to note that the horse has not always been the sturdy, large, hoofed animal you see and know today. Fifty million years ago, it was a tiny multi-toed mammal – no larger than a medium-sized pup. Since its evolution, humans have recognized and have taken advantage of the great power and strength the horse possesses, putting it to use for various purposes.

Reasons For Raising Horses

Horseback riding is one of the oldest uses of horses since its domestication. Horses were also used to pull wheels of chariots, carts, and wagons in medieval times. Horses were a predominant means of transportation and communication in ancient times. It was also commonly used in warfare and had increasing relevance in society as it became a standard of wealth.

In the past, movement on foot was the only means of transporting resources and communicating with other people. So, you can imagine how revolutionary it was when horse riding came on the scene. Goods and places, once inaccessible or too time-consuming to transport, quickly became available as riders can move easily and faster than people on foot.

Fast-forward to the present day, and horseback riding is still very much relevant. They might not have as much social importance as they did back then since they were the only means of transportation, and ow, we have various vehicles and machinery to replace them. However, there are still a lot of uses for horses that technology is yet to replace. For example, mounted police are still in use by various countries in the world. Although their work is sometimes ceremonial, they are often used by the police for other functions such as crowd control or patrol in places inaccessible for police vehicles.

You may have seen one or more mounted police in your vicinity or at an event. During crowd control, mounted officers are more visible than those on the ground or in cars and inform people of the presence of the police. This helps to deter crimes and helps officers easily spot offenders as the height of the horse allows the police to see farther and wider.

In today's world, equestrian sport is perhaps the most notable application of horses. There are two major styles of riding horses: the English riding style and the Western riding style. You might be wondering what makes them different. Well, history helps provide an answer.

The Western riding originated from the ranches and was practiced by cowboys of mid and southwest United States. Cattle ranchers used horses in controlling the cattle, and this required the rider to be skillful at controlling and maneuvering the horse while riding at high speed. Specialized heavy saddles were created for the riders to help spread their weight on the horse and allow them to ride for long and across uneven roads without feeling uncomfortable.

The reins tied around their neck and a bit in the horse's mouth enabled the rider to control the horse with just one hand. Some equestrian disciplines that require western riding style include roping, reining, trail-riding, cutting, speed games, and so on.

The English riding style, on the other hand, originated from England and has its root in military and cavalry training. As equestrian sports competition began, this riding style was passed down and adopted for sporting purposes. Over the years, there have been changes to the style – but the basic principles remain the same.

Since the primary purpose of the English riding style is competitions, the saddles are designed to aid mobility for both the horse and its rider. They are lighter and smaller than the western saddles. The reins are directly connected to the horse's mouth and are to be held with both hands. Examples of equestrian competitions in which this riding style is used are dressage, show jumping, hunting, polo, mounted games, and many more.

Use of Horses For Their Therapeutic Benefits

Horseback riding is not only fun but has been proven to be therapeutic. It is a form of recreational therapy aimed at improving an individual's mental, physical, and emotional health through different horse riding techniques.

Since riding a horse can obviously be done only in an outdoor environment, you are bound to spend more in the open, breathing in nature's fresh air. The feeling of freedom and independence that accompanies riding your horse in the wild is stimulating and second to none. Horse riding is a creative and helpful way to take a break from your typical everyday routine.

Coupled with this, horses are intelligent and emotional creatures capable of developing a bond with their owners and caretakers. Raising, riding, and caring for a horse avails you the opportunity to form a pure and unadulterated bond with it. These gentle yet majestic creatures are faithful and trustworthy and can easily become a man's best friend.

Additional Health Benefits Associated with Horse Riding

Core Muscle Strengthening

Consistently riding horses is a form of exercise for your core muscles. Your chest, abdomen, and lower back make up your core muscles. By engaging them while riding, you are actually strengthening the muscles present there. This simultaneously helps you stay balanced on the horse.

Flexibility and Balance

Balancing is one of the first skills to master if you want to ride a horse properly and avoid falling off. The more accustomed you get to riding your horse, the easier it becomes to balance yourself either on a saddle or bareback. This balance is usually evident in the improvement of your body posture. The continuous exercise of galloping helps to improve your body flexibility, even when you are not riding.

Improved Coordination

First-time horse riders will find it difficult to move or direct the horse as they please because of the high level of coordination required. You will need to apply leg pressure, rein pressure, and move your body all – at the same time – when riding and directing your horse. The more consistently you ride, the more your coordination skills improve. Soon enough, you will learn how to simultaneously use individual parts of your body to move your horse in any direction, and this can be applied to other activities as well.

Enhances Mental Strength

Horse riding is extremely beneficial for your mental health. For starters, it is a soothing and relaxing exercise that clears your mind and improves your mood. Horses are emotional creatures with stress-relieving abilities. Also, interacting with the horse will require you to learn different cues that aid in directing and understanding your horse. Your confidence level can significantly improve just by gaining mastery over this huge and beautiful animal. Besides all these, raising a horse is a great feat and gives you a sense of fulfillment.

Muscle Tone and Stable Strength

While riding a horse, your inner thighs and pelvic are engaged the most as you need to position yourself constantly in rhythm with the horse's cadence. Taking care of the horse in the stables requires you to lift heavy items that can be initially tasking. Still, as you engage in these activities, you can increase your cardiovascular capability and build what is popularly known as *stable strength.*

Improves Problem-Solving Skills

Problem-solving is another skill associated with raising horses. This is because horses can be quite challenging and unpredictable sometimes, especially if it is unfamiliar territory. As a rider, you have to learn to think critically and come up with solutions that allow you to safeguard yourself and keep your horse under control. Each problem you can solve with your horse helps you develop a reservoir of skills that can come handy soon.

Use of Horses for Farm Work

In some parts of the world, horses are raised strictly for farm work purposes. Although machinery and other forms of equipment have taken over much of farm and agricultural related labor, horses are still the preferred means of work in certain places. A common reason for this is the type of land or soil present. Some terrains can easily be destroyed by the use of machines or vehicles; to preserve such natural reserves, animals are used.

Also, in cases where the land is too rough for vehicles to pass through, horses or other farm animals are employed. Last, specific agricultural practices like cultivating and logging are best carried out by horses or other working animals to prevent loss of natural habitat through the use of fossil fuels.

Historically, farm animals have been in use for centuries. Long before any technological advancement was made in agriculture, animals were used in carrying out farm labor. Due to the hard labor required on the farmlands, a specific horse breed was desired for this cause. While the lighter and spirited horses were suitable for riding, the bulkier and patient ones were preferred by farmers to be used on ranches and farmlands. These horses are called *draft horses*. Plowing and transportation of heavy loads are some tasks of a draft horse.

Raising and caring for draft horses differs somewhat from raising a horse for leisure. Because they are work animals, your main focus will be on grooming them to work efficiently. Shoeing and feeding are essential and costly because, as opposed to riding horses, draft horses require their shoes for labor. Draft horses have a slower rate of metabolism in comparison with riding horses but need a large amount of food due to their bulky size.

Fertilizer

Here is a fascinating fact about horses you probably did not know. The average horse eats 2 percent of its bodyweight and excretes about 50 pounds of wet manure between 4 to 13 times daily. Add that all up, and in a year, you will have about 9.1 tons of manure. However, the waste product of your horse does not necessarily have to *go to waste*.

Horse feces contain a lot of nutrients beneficial for plant growth. As a horse owner, you need not worry much about buying fertilizer for your grass. Your horse is a convenient source of fertilizer! Horses are herbivores, and so their manure contains necessary nutrients and organic matter that plants require for growth. It is an economical way of getting fertilizers for plants, and you can also produce enough to sell.

Composting the manure helps to keep the nutrients in and gets rid of bacteria or weed seed present. Compositing the manure simply means allowing it to sit for a while before use, which ensures the proper breakdown of the organic matter present in it.

Horse manure comprises nitrogen, phosphorus, and potassium, with nitrogen produced in the highest amount. Although these nutrients are extremely beneficial for soil and crop production, if not properly managed, they can also have adverse effects on the environment.

As a horse owner, you will need to acquaint yourself with your state regulations guiding proper management of horse manure to ensure its optimal use and reduce pollution. The best way to do this is by having a plan for horse manure management. Consider the number of horses you have per acre of land, the estimated amount of manure produced yearly, and the means of manure storage or removal.

Horses for Entertainment and Ceremonial Uses

Horses are also used for entertainment, in the form of shows and to portray historical or past events. These are regal and handsome creatures whose gracefulness is unparalleled with any other animal, with a majestic appearance that makes them very suitable for royal or official ceremonies and functions.

A horse-drawn carriage and riding horses are especially useful for these occasions. Weddings, inaugurations, and tourist attractions make up some functions you will find horses being used in present-day society. In some other cultures, horses are usually the main events at parades and festivals. Circuses and theater shows also make use of horses in some of their performances. These horses are often trained to perform various tricks solely for entertainment.

Films and literature set in historic or medieval times often make use of horses while trying to re-enact the way people lived in bygone days. Horses were the most common means of transportation for many centuries, and so their presence in historical films are pivotal. Unsurprisingly, warfare has also witnessed the uniqueness of the horse from other animals. Like other human activities the horse has participated in, it played a huge role at war fronts, transporting both goods and men and even engaging in the bitter rivalry and bloodshed.

Horses As Companions and Pets

Of the different roles that horses play in man's life, being a companion is one of the most revered positions. When you ride a horse frequently, over time, as you get used to each other, there is a high tendency of becoming attached to the horse and forming a bond. Most often, this bond is based on trust. The horse is an intelligent animal with a mind of its own, so for you to train, control, and ride it, mutual trust is required on both sides.

Coupled with this is the emotional quality horses possess. If you spend time petting and being around your horse, it can improve your emotional health and be a stress-reliever. Horses have an uncanny ability to recognize emotions and empathize with you.

Horses are social animals, and so it is not uncommon to find them moving in herds, especially feral horses. If you are raising a working horse alone in a barn or stable, there is a tendency that your horse may feel lonely or isolated. As a horse owner, you can try to recreate this need for a social structure by rearing what is commonly known as companion horses. Companion horses do not necessarily need to be ridden as they mainly provide company and succor to the working horse. The companion horse also doubles as a pet.

Horses For Leisure and Sport

There are many leisure and sporting activities within which horses play primary and pivotal roles. Equestrian activities are fairly common today and serve as a major reason to raise horses. There are different equestrian sporting activities, each with its specific breed of horses. Some of the competitive equestrian sports include events, horse racing, dressage, rodeo, polo, reining, tent pegging, and many more. These sports are very different and require a varying number of technical and specialized skills for each one, so different breeds of horses are used in different sports.

You might be surprised to know that most of the horse breeds today came about because of well-ordered specific breeding. To raise a sports horse, there are so many breeds to select from. As you read further in the book, you will get to know more about the different horse breeds.

There are also non-competitive sports that you can train your horse to participate in and if you are not a sports person, simply riding your horse in the open field or ranch is adventurous and exhilarating.

Important Considerations Before Purchasing a Horse

People raise horses for one or more of the reasons listed above, but whatever your reason might be, you will need to consider important factors before purchasing a horse. A horse is a big investment you most likely cannot return, so it is wise that you carefully weigh your options before making a selection.

1. Cost: Taking care of horses is quite a responsibility. Before you buy a horse, you need to consider the total costs required to raise it – and not just the initial purchase cost. The average horse has a lifespan of about 20 to 30 years, and so you will be taking care of the horse for a long time. Feeding, shelter, health care, riding equipment, hoof care, tack and supplies, training and riding lessons, emergency expenses, and many more make up the long-term cost you will need to spend to care for and raise a horse.

2. Commitment: As previously stated, horses are a great responsibility, and so raising one will require care and attention. Be ready to commit enough time to care for the horse. Riding, grooming, feeding, and training your horse is part of your duties as a horse owner, and they need to be done often. You should not leave your horse without attention for more than a day, as they require frequent exercise.

3. Shelter: Depending on how many horses you plan on buying(and their purpose), you will need to provide suitable shelter for it. Housing your horse on your own land gives you the advantage of easy access to feeding and daily grooming, but the daily maintenance of horse care is a daunting task that comes with this choice. Local stables offer boarding facilities to horse owners that assist in horse care and offer other amenities. There is also the added advantage of meeting other horse owners at the stable. Consider which option works best for you before buying the horse.

4. The Horse: Horses come in various breeds, sizes, ages, pedigree, and levels of training, and each feature should be considered e before making your purchase. The purpose you want to use your horse will help you narrow down your options. For riding horses, you will need to be more specific as there are various riding styles suitable for different breeds. Preferably, purchase a horse that has a significant level of training, unless you plan on doing that yourself. Horses have different personalities, so select a horse that suits your temperamental preference.

Once you can select the horse most suitable to your liking, the next thing to do is to ensure a thorough and complete health examination is carried out by a certified veterinarian. The veterinarian should be well acquainted with the specific breed and designated purpose. This examination is very important as you will be provided with an in-depth knowledge of the horse's medical history. Such information will aid you in making your final decision.

Raising a horse is a rewarding yet challenging task. As a horse owner, you have a lot of responsibility to ensure you groom and care for your horse properly. Horses may be huge and stubborn sometimes, but they still need a confident, tender-yet-assertive owner to direct and take care of them. This book is focused on making you that kind of owner.

Chapter Two: Selecting The Right Breed

There are about 400 horse breeds known to man, each one with its own uniqueness and specializations. Equestrian competitions capitalize on these differences and can thus engage in a variety of sporting activities. As a horse owner, you must know the differences between breeds and their specializations. In this chapter, we will describe some of the most popular horse breeds, their qualities, and their usage.

Arabian

With its unique arched shaped neck and high graceful tail carriage, you can easily identify the Arabian horse anywhere. It originated from Arab and is one of the oldest breeds whose lineage dates to over 4,000 years ago. It is versatile, has strong stamina, and is popularly known for its endurance riding.

The Arabian has a height of 14 hands to 16 hands, (56 inches – 64 inches), and a light bodyweight of 800 – 100 pounds. Arabians are also known for their amicable temperament, which makes them quick to learn and easily attached to humans. They are widely used in many equestrian activities like horse racing, dressage, showjumping, endurance riding, and many more. They are ideal for leisure riding and can be found on ranches, when not in sports competitions.

Thoroughbred

Have you noticed a very popular fast and specific breed used in various equestrian competitions? It is very likely to be a fierce and agile Thoroughbred. Thoroughbred horses come from a lineage of likewise agile and swift stallions like the Arabian and the Turkoman. It is considered a part of the "hot-blooded" breed of horses because of its strength, agility, and speed. They mostly come in dark or gray colors and have a height range of about 15.2 hands (62 inches) to 17.0 hands (68 inches).

Some easily recognizable features of the Thoroughbred include a well-chiseled head, long neck, deep chest, short back, lean body, and long legs. The Thoroughbred is a very spirited and athletic horse, which makes it a perfect fit for various equestrian sports competitions. It is also commonly used to bred horses for other riding sports like polo, dressage, showjumping, and others.

Appaloosa

Best known for its spotted and brightly colored body, the Appaloosa is a very popular breed in North America with a unique heritage. Originally domesticated by the Nez-Perce natives, it was used in hunting and as a war animal. Its distinct spots and color resulted from different cross breeds over the centuries. Uneven skin color, striped hooves, and visible white sclera in the eyes are traits that identify an Appaloosa.

There are various body types attributed to an Appaloosa breed because of the different other breeds that make up its lineage. Still, the average size is usually between 950 – 1250 pounds and 14 hands (56 inches) to 15 hands (60 inches) in height. It is commonly used as a stock horse for controlling cattle on the ranch, and it also features in various western riding competitions. Leisure riding, trail riding, and middle distance are a few other uses this versatile and intelligent horse is great for.

Morgan

The Morgan Horse is a fine and peculiar horse with a regal carriage that makes it befitting for various ceremonial functions and as coach horses. It was named after its first owner, Justin Morgan, and has been used for breeding other horses. You can recognize a Morgan horse with its confident gait, refined and muscular build, strong hindquarters, and high tail carriage. Morgan breeds are very strong and have a standard height of 14.1 hands (57 inches) to 15.2 hands (62 inches). The Morgan is commonly used for both English and Western riding sport, leisure riding, and also in equestrian sports competitions. It is renowned for its distinct personality, quiet disposition, intelligence, and boldness.

American Quarter Horse

The quarter horse is one of the most popular horse breeds in America. It was bred from the Thoroughbred horse and is very versatile. You may recognize it at rodeos or racehorse shows by its ability to move swiftly across short distances. It has a short but refined head, sturdy body structure, and rounded hindquarters. The height of a typical Quarter horse ranges from 14 hands (56 inches) to 16 hands (64 inches). It is best known on the sports field as a sprinter, outrunning other breeds in races of a quarter-mile distance or less. It is also commonly used as a ranch horse, and its petite body makes it very suitable for technical and skillful activities like barrel racing, calf roping, and other western riding competitions.

Standardbred

A Standardbred horse is a versatile North American horse breed whose prowess is evident in horse harnessing and several other equestrian disciplines. Like other horse breeds, it comes from a lineage of other stallion breeds, notably the thoroughbred and

Morgan, among others. It is agile, swift, and has a muscular, strong build slightly heavier than the thoroughbred.

Standardbreds have an average height of 14 hands (56 inches) to 17 hands (68 inches) and weigh between 800 to 1000 pounds. You will find them easily in harness racing competitions as they are the fastest trotting horse breed known to man. Other uses of the Standardbred include leisure riding, horse shows, ranch horses, and, most important, they are used for breeding other horses.

Percheron

The Percheron is a French horse that belongs to a popular breed of horses known as draft breeds. They are peculiar for their rugged and sturdy build. They have served as war horses, stagecoaches, and farm animals because of their great strength and muscular bulk. You can easily tell a Percheron horse out by its bulky and muscular legs, broad chest, huge size, and docile personality. They are commonly called "cold-blooded" because of their calm disposition.

The height and weight of the Percheron differ for various countries, and they are widely used as workhorses. They are used at parades, for agricultural purposes, to pull heavy loads and are crossbred with other lighter horses to improve stamina and produce medium-sized horses for other purposes.

Welsh Ponies

Most people know what a pony is, at least by their description. Ponies are miniature horses. They are a class of horse breeds with a height that is not over 14.2 hands (58 inches) at maturity. They are thus shorter than the average horse and preferably the best option for children riders. They have their origin from Wales with the Arabian and Thoroughbred horses as part of their lineage.

They come in four types distinguished by their height, the shortest being about 11 hands (44 inches) and 16 hands (64 inches) being the tallest. Their strong and easy gait movements often characterize them. Welsh ponies are highly intelligent animals with great speed and endurance. They are used for many purposes, namely as work animals, for leisure riding, and in equestrian sports competition. They are especially good at dressage, endurance racing, and driving.

Tennessee Walking Horse

Also known as the *Tennessee Walker*, this unique horse breed belongs to a class of horse breeds commonly known as gaited breeds. The gaited breed is a distinct class of horses bred for their ability to go at an easy pace with a four-beat rhythm. Their sauntered gait makes them ideal for older riders or just anyone looking for a smooth ride.

The Tennessee Walker is an elegant and sturdy animal with an average height of 14.3 hands (59 inches) to 17 hands (68 inches) and a weight of about 900 to 1200 pounds. They are most popular for their calm nature and running-walk ability. They are commonly used in horse shows, trail riding events, and for pleasure riding.

Hanoverian

The Hanoverian horse falls into the category of "warm-blooded" horse breeds. They are usually developed by breeding a "hot-blooded" type with a "cold-blooded" stallion. The Hanoverian is a special warmblood that originated from Germany. It was refined with Thoroughbred blood to make it more agile and athletic. The result turned out to be utterly successful.

Elegant, strong, and athletic, the Hanoverian breed is a versatile, spirited horse with a pleasant ambiance. It was formerly used in the military and as a coach horse. Today, it is one of the most popular and widely used sport horses as it holds medals in all equestrian Olympic sports. The average height of a Hanoverian breed is between 15.3 hands (63 inches) to 17.2 hands (70 inches). It is used mainly as a sports animal but can also be ridden for pleasure.

Mustang

Mustangs are breeds of horses you will mostly find in the wild. They are free-roaming horses originally brought to North America by the Spanish. You can effortlessly recognize them by the short but sturdy frame, wide head, and small muzzle. The typical Mustang has a height of about 14 hands (56 inches) to 15 hands (60 inches). They are best known for their endurance, strength, and surefootedness. They are used in horse race competitions, trail riding, pleasure riding, and also as farm animals.

American Paint Horse

One of the first things you will notice about the American Paint Horse is its rich and colorful coat. Every paint horse has a unique color of white and another equine color. Its lineage can be traced back to the Thoroughbred and Quarter horse breed.

A typical American Paint Horse has an average height of 14 to 16 hands (56 inches to 64 inches) and a weight of about 950 to 1,200 pounds. Some of its other distinctive features include a muscular body, a low center of gravity that allows easy maneuvering, and strong hindquarters for swift movement. It is frequently used in western equestrian competitions like show jumping and reining.

Haflinger

If you see a group of somewhat short horses all chestnut in color, they probably are the Haflinger horse breed. Originally from Austria, the history of the Haflinger can be traced back to the middle ages. They are strongly built, elegant, and have a beautiful flaxen mare.

The average height for the Haflinger is 13.2 to 15 hands (54 to 60 inches, respectively), and it mainly exists in chestnut color. It has a smooth, rhythmic gait that allows it to provide an energetic yet soothing ride.

It is suitable for under saddle activities and can also be used as a draft or packhorse. Some of the equestrian competitions you will find a Haflinger engaged in include show jumping, vaulting, dressage, endurance, and trail riding. It is also suitable for therapeutic and leisure riding.

American Saddlebred

Another member of the gaited breed, the American Saddlebred Horse, is a brilliant horse breed that originated from the United States. Its lineage can be traced back to riding horses of ambling gaits in the British Isles. It has the Morgan and Thoroughbred blood as part of its ancestry. The Saddlebred is characterized by the regal carriage of its muscular and lean frame.

A very beautiful and lively horse, the typical Saddlebred has an average height of 15 to 17 hands (60 to 68 inches, respectively). Gentle and elegant, you can clearly spot a Saddlebred by its superior movement and smooth gait. It is best used as a show horse but also features in other equestrian competitions such as combined driving, dressage, and saddle seat riding.

Hackney Horse

The Hackney horse breed has its roots in Britain and was developed to be a riding horse with a perfect trot. It has strong stamina and an attractive frame. It is popularly used as a carriage horse due to its stylish and superior movement.

The height of a typical Hackney horse is between 14. 2 to 16.2 hands (58 inches to 64 inches respectively), and they weigh about 1000 pounds. Its high-speed trot and elegant appearance usually characterize it.

You can differentiate a Hackney horse from other similar breeds by its well-defined features, attentive ears, eyes, and a naturally high tail carriage. It is mostly used as a carriage horse and in competitive sports, can be found in harness racing and driving events. Its powerful hindquarters help provide a comfortable and rhythmic stride that allows for pleasure and therapeutic riding.

Selecting The Right Horse Breed

Horses are emotional and intelligent creatures with a personality and mind of their own. When selecting a horse, you need to consider your preferences alongside the horse's temperament and disposition. The purpose for which you want to raise the horse, your level of expertise and your riding experience should all be considered.

If you are a beginner just starting out with horses, you will need a patient and willing horse; one that is intelligent, learns easily, and has a pleasant ambiance. The American Quarter Horse, Tennessee Walking Horse, Shire Horse, and Morgan all fall into this category. Ponies also make great beginner horses for children or those under 5.5 ft.

Cold-blooded horse breeds are calm, approachable, and friendly. They are often very huge and lack the excitement you will normally find among sports horses. Their gentle disposition makes them ideal for farm work and labor. Examples of cold-blooded breeds include coldblooded trotter, Percheron, Belgian Draft, and Clydesdale.

Warm-blooded horse breeds are versatile and vivacious animals. They are a combination of cold-blooded and hot-blooded breeds, with the friendly and approachable ambiance of cold-bloods and the strength and agility of hot-bloods. You can train and use them for sports competitions with little difficulty. The American Quarter Horse, Appaloosa, Tennessee Walker, Mustang, and Cleveland bay are examples of warmbloods.

If you are looking for energetic and fast-paced horses, go for hot-blooded breeds. They are frequently used as sports horses because of the high level of energy and agility they possess. They are hard to control, highly temperamental, and are more suited for experienced owners. Examples of hot-bloods include Arabian, Thoroughbred, and Morgan. They are often used in systematic breeding to produce other horse breeds with specific features.

You can check out the Hanoverian, American Saddlebred, Paint horse, Arabian and Morgan, if you are looking for horse breeds with poise and elegance. These breeds have a muscular and well-defined frame, have a majestic carriage, and are ideal for pleasure riding.

Chapter Three: Bringing Your Horse Home

Having completed the first stage of selecting and purchasing your dream horse, it is time to begin your role as a horse owner. Understandably you will be feeling nervous and excited about the prospect, so the best way to deal with those nerves is by proper planning. In this chapter, you will learn about the necessary tasks involved in bringing your horse home and what to do once it arrives. Remember, your horse is moving into new and unfamiliar surroundings, so you need to ensure it feels safe and comfortable.

What to do before your Horse comes Home

Before your horse arrives, prepare a form of shelter for it. You can use either house the horse on your property if you have enough land or in a local stable nearby. If you have the stable on your property, you will need to clean and inspect it before the horse arrives. The fence, stall walls, and gates should be in good condition and free of any hazardous item. The stall should not be too tight or cornered so as not to make your horse feel trapped. It is a new environment, and it is important to lessen the anxiety of your horse. Make repairs where necessary and ensure the fences are visible and of adequate height for the horse, especially if it is an outdoor enclosure. Your horse can try to jump over the fence, so you need to take all precautions. The stall door should be strong and sturdy enough to hold the horse in. If you plan on boarding your horse at a local stable, make proper inquiries to ensure your horse will be kept safe and comfortable.

Ready Stable Checklist

✔ Select appropriate shelter

✔ Clean and inspect stable

✔ Make necessary repairs

✔ Purchase Necessary Equipment

The phrase "*necessary equipment*" varies based on your purpose of raising the horse, but there are essential items every horse owner must-have.

● Feed and water basin.

● Lead rope and head collar

● Saddle, bridle, and bit.

● Splint and tendon boots.

● Horse grooming kit. This should include a curry comb, water, and body brush, mane comb, hoof brush, sponge, hoof oil, fly repellent, and sweat scraper. You can put them all in a single box to ease convenience.

● First aid kit. In case of any injury or emergency, be ready to attend to your horse before the veterinarian arrives. Your first aid kit should contain bandages, cotton wool, tweezers, wound cleanser, scissors, antibiotic spray, thermometer, and veterinarian emergency numbers.

Vaccinations

Before bringing your horse home, make sure a certified veterinarian thoroughly examines it, preferably one familiar with the breed. There are different vaccinations available for horses to help them maintain good health. As a horse owner, you must ensure the protection of your horse by keeping it up to date with vaccines, even before it arrives at your home. Horses, if not well cared for, can fall ill due to infections or diseases. Your horse will rely on you to keep it in good shape.

Update Vaccine Checklist

✔ Find out the necessary information on horse vaccination.

✔ Get your horse thoroughly examined.

✔ Get your horse vaccinated.

Feeding

If your horse has a previous owner, it will be wise to get all the information about your new horse from him/her. Discover what kind of feed your horse prefers and how much hay and feed it consumes daily. Purchase the hay and feed for your horse before you bring it home. If you have a particular feed you want your horse to eat, do not force it on your horse. Instead, gradually introduce the feed, and with the time, you will win him over.

Water is essential to horses of all breeds. The average horse consumes about seven gallons of water each day. It is, therefore, imperative you provide access to fresh and clean water for your horse. Because your horse is new to your environment, there is a tendency for it to react negatively to drinking foreign water. One way to combat is by using the same or a similar basin that your horse is familiar with. If your barn or stable has an automated water system, your new horse might be unfamiliar with it, and can take a while to figure it out. During that period, you will need to provide clean water in a means that your horse is familiar with, such as a basin or tub.

Feeding Checklist

✔ Ask the previous owner for feed preference.

✔ Buy enough hay and feed.

✔ Provide access to fresh water.

✔ Put fresh water in a familiar basin for the horse.

Transporting the Horse

So, you have gotten the stable set up, purchased the equipment, vaccinated your horse, and bought essential food items. Now, it is time to bring the horse home. Depending on the distance between your horse's location and your home, you can transport your horse via land or air. Whichever means of transportation you use, try to take the shortest route possible to make the journey less strenuous. The best way to transport your horse on land is by using a horse trailer. You can always rent one if you don't have one of your own. Employing the services of a professional horse moving company will help reduce the stress on your horse during the travel.

Check the trailer before the travel day to make sure it is in good condition and comfortable for your horse. The size of the trailer should be big enough for your horse to lower its head, and the floor should be non-slip. Stop the vehicle at intervals for the horse to feed and rest if it is a long distance. For safety and to also aid you in loading the horse, make use of a lead rope or halter to tie the horse, but not too tight, so it does not get uncomfortable. Hauling a horse in a transport vehicle can be really stressful as horses are wary of confined spaces. To avoid such, train your horse to climb in and out of the trailer before the traveling day.

Transportation Checklist

✔ Research the best mode to bring the horse home.

✔ Hire a professional horse moving services.

✔ Inspect the transportation vehicle.

✔ Plan the trip taking the shortest route possible.

✔ Carry enough water and feed for the horse.

✔ Get travel boots for your horse.

✔ Train the horse to load in and out of the trailer before moving day.

Settling The Horse in its New Home

After a long trip (or maybe a short one), you have finally arrived at your destination-home, with your horse. The first few days and weeks of your horse's arrival is important in helping it adjust to its new home and getting familiar with you. Here are important steps that can help you settle your horse in its new home.

Step 1: Getting your horse out of the trailer can be a daunting task as the horse is bound to be nervous and reluctant. If you have trained your horse on how to load and offload a trailer, it might not be as hard. Preferably – and especially if this is your first horse – have an experienced person around to guide and assist you.

Step 2: Gently and patiently guide your horse to the barn and remove his traveling boots. Provide clean water and hay in his stall. If you have other horses, position your new horse so that he can see the other horses.

If you will be placing your new horse in a pasture with a padlock, consider walking him around the fence, so he becomes accustomed to the boundary and knows where to find feed and water.

Step 3: When you want to turn out your horse for the first time, protect him with boots, so he doesn't hurt himself or get hurt by other horses. Keep your horse in a closed stall or pasture, facing other horses. This will help him interact with the other horses.

Leave your new horse in his stall for the first few days. This will help him relax and feel safe. Ensure he is feeding and drinking water properly. Check his temperature regularly and if you have any worries, consult a veterinarian. Since he is not exercising, you can reduce his feed to avoid him having colic.

Step 4: While he is in his stall, you can get more familiar with him by grooming and spending time with him. After a few days, you can take your new horse out for a walk around the grounds. Use a rope and bridle to lead him. Allow him to explore his new environment while keeping an eye on him.

If you have more than two other horses, it is advisable not to introduce your new horse to the whole herd all at once. Rather, as the weeks go by, introduce to them one after the other. Keep him away from the others but not totally isolated, as horses are social creatures and need company too.

Step 5: Once you are certain your new horse has spent considerable time with you and is more familiar with the grounds and other horses, you can consider letting him out with the whole herd. Before doing so, make sure there is enough pasture for all horses to graze comfortably. If the pasture is too small, there is likely to be a fight for space and grass among the horses – you don't want that! The general rule of thumb is to have one acre of land pasture per horse.

Step 6: When you decide to let your new horse out with the whole herd, you will need to be around and watch carefully, so there are no brawls or injuries sustained. There is no need to rush with the introductions. Observe your new horse for any signs of stress or mistreatment by the older horses.

Spend time with the new horse by grooming and getting more acquainted with what he likes.

Step 7: Riding your new horse for the first time is usually a thrilling experience for any horse owner. Before you start riding, your horse should already feel comfortable with you and the environment. Do not force it but be slow and gentle with the horse.

This is still part of the process of getting to know your horse and vice versa for him. Ride just a short distance for the first few times, doing your best to keep it simple. In time, you will both get used to each other.

Step 8: Owning a horse creates an avenue to make new friends – fellow horse owners! Get to meet other horse owners, trade stories, and get tips and insights on how best to care for your horse. Borrow from the experience of seasoned horse riders in training and keep your horse safe.

You can learn a lot by listening to other people's stories and experiences.

Step 9: Most important, keep in touch with your horse's previous owner or seller. Let the person know improvements the horse is making and ask questions when unsure of certain behavioral traits.

Keep a close eye on the health of your horse and consult a veterinarian when necessary.

Chapter Four: Horse Handling And Bonding

Before going further, it is paramount that you understand the mindset and behavioral patterns of the horse to improve and develop your relationship with it. As it was stated earlier in the book, horses are highly intelligent animals with a mind of their own. When you can grasp the way a horse thinks, you can then modify its behavior and train it.

The first – and most important – thing you should know about the horse is that it is a *prey animal*. This means that its actions and thought pattern is predicated upon staying alive. Consider other prey animals you know, rabbits, sheep, and so on; they all possess a common instinct to survive, and this is often seen in their behavior and reaction to what they consider as threats.

The horse, like these animals, understands that to stay alive, it has to be vigilant and watchful of perceived threat or danger. This is why you can find your horse becoming anxious at seemingly unimportant things like walking through a small pool of water, climbing into a trailer, being in a novel situation, or hearing unexpected sounds in the environment. Their first instinct is to flee to protect themselves. This is an example of the self-preservation skills they have acquired over the years.

To the horse, the human is a predator, unless proven otherwise. Predators, unlike prey, are less focused on surviving and more on achieving their goal. The prey (the horse), on the other hand, just wants to live. He runs away, not necessarily out of fear of getting hurt but to save his life. Knowing this about your horse can help you relate better with him. Now that you know how the typical horse sees you, your aim should be to gain his trust by building a relationship with him. This is usually the first step towards training your horse.

Horses are social animals who live in packs and have a hierarchical structure. This structure is pivotal because it allows for a dominant and reliable leader who makes the horse feel safe. They all respect the leader because he provides food, guidance, and safety for all. He eats and drinks first, while the others wait, and he exerts his dominance assertively by claiming his space. The other horses understand this assertion and submit them to the authority. If you have more than one horse, you can take time out to study your herd and try to identify the dominant one.

You need to know that horses naturally desire leadership, whether they are alone or in a herd. As a horse owner, you must provide such leadership, or the horse will take the reins. The bedrock of a successful horse-human relationship begins with you taking the lead. When the horse sees you as a reliable leader, it respects your authority and follows your direction, just like the social hierarchy of the herds. Asserting dominance is how you become the leader of the herd. This assertion is not done with violence but calmly and firmly. This is most often done by either inhibiting or allowing movement. For instance, if your horse wants to move in a certain direction, you can stop his movement by applying pressure using his reins and releasing it when he does your bidding. It must be you who controls its movement and not the other way around.

The more dominance you exert, the more willing your horse will be to follow your leadership. When your horse is willing to follow you, training it for any purpose will not be difficult. Your horse must see you as a confident and consistent leader. Take charge when situations arise and give direction to your horse. Horses have two major needs; safety and comfort. Lack of comfort for the horse can range from mild things like a piece of moving plastic to dangerous situations like a predator threat; both are equally terrifying for him. He does not feel safe and will seek to get rid of the discomfort. But when there is a clearly defined leader, the horse feels safe and secured. As a horse owner, aim for making your horse feel safe.

Safe Handling of Horses

Safe handling of horses refers to guidelines and rules. Every horse owner has to know, for his/her own safety and the safety of the horse. The horse is physically stronger than a human, so it is very important to take safety measures while tending to him. Like it was stated earlier, horses are prey animals whose first instinct to an unfamiliar stimulus (puddle, enclosed space, unexpected noise) or discomfort is to defend themselves and flee. Therefore, they should be handled calmly and gently. These safety guidelines help a horse owner attend to his/her horse in the best way possible so as not to get hurt by the horse. They might seem like a lot initially for the beginner horse owner, but not to worry; you will quickly get used to them with time.

1. Always approach the horse from a visible point, preferably the front, so he is not caught unaware of your presence. Avoid touching or patting him from behind as this can easily startle or scare him, causing him to react aggressively.

2. Wear strong and protective footwear while attending to your horse to avoid getting hurt if he steps on you. Causal, open, or thin shoes should not be worn in the barn, stable, or around your horse.

3. When cleaning your horse's stall, grooming, or preparing for a ride, keep your horse tied up. It is dangerous to let him freely roam the barn.

4. Horses are much different from dogs or other pets that can be fed with your hands. They can mistake your hands for food and bite you, along with whatever you are feeding them. To feed your horse treats, do it from a bucket.

5. You should never stand directly behind a horse. It has powerful hindquarters that can knock you out with a single kick. To clean his tail, stand at one side, and carefully pull the tail to you.

6. If you are cleaning the hooves of your horse or you want to put bandages on, do not kneel or squat; bend low instead. If the horse makes any movement, you can quickly get out of harm's way.

7. Tie your horse with simple and easy to remove knots like the quick release knot so that if your horse feels uncomfortable or threatened, it can quickly break free. Hard or complicated knots can make you feel constrained, and he might react negatively.

8. Use a lead rope and halter to safe lead and direct your horse. Do not place your hands or fingers through any of the tack equipment as you can easily get injured by sudden movements of the horse.

9. Do not stand beside your horse unseen. Always make sure your horse sees and knows who you are while grooming or just talk with him.

10. Do not clean out the stall of your horse while your horse is inside. Put him in another stall or take him to pasture.

11. Understand your horse's body language while interacting with him. Horses communicate with their eyes, ears, and tails. Continuous movement of their ears signals nervousness, while flat ears indicate annoyance or anger, which can lead to an attack. If his ears are relaxed, he is relaxed also.

12. Horses learn a lot from their owner's overt and covert behavior. They are good judges of mood and can detect fear and anxiety. While handling your horse, you must be confident and bold.

13. Do not tie the lead rope or reins around your hands or body part. It can be disastrous if the horse moves suddenly without direction. Never tie yourself in any way to a horse.

14. Stall and barn doors should be wide enough for your horse to pass through without feeling crowded or tight. If you have to pass through a narrow door with your horse, lead the way by going in first, then stand at one side and allow him to come in.

Bonding with Horses

Horses make excellent companions. They are emotional, therapeutic, and easy to talk to. While this easy camaraderie seems enchanting, it does not come with little effort. For a horse owner, bonding with your horse begins with a mutual trust from both sides. Your horse has to learn to trust you to keep him safe and comfortable. You, the horse owner, have to handle your horse in a gentle, caring, and sincere manner.

If you are a beginner with horses and you are wondering why you do not seem to bond with your horse, maybe you are not doing things correctly. While interacting and spending time with your horse, there are tips and tricks you can employ to aid foster the relationship between both of you. These tips, when implemented, help you and your horse develop a close and long-lasting relationship.

Be a Firm, Open-Minded, and Assertive Leader

The importance of you being a leader to your horse has been explained earlier, so it should not come as a surprise to you how pivotal this is. Being a firm and assertive leader makes your horse respect your authority and dominance. He will treat you like the head of the herd and follow your lead. Notwithstanding, be open-minded and fair. Treat your horse right by using consistent cues he can understand and follow. Horses are not logical thinkers, so don't have unrealistic expectations from them. Horses have a good memory and can tell when they are not being treated right. They can become resistant and stubborn in such cases. It is best to begin your relationship on a good foot.

Spend Quality Time with Them

Your relationship with your horse should go beyond work or training hours. To develop a bond with your horse, you need to show him you are interested in him and not just the work he can do. Visit him in the stable often and take him out for walks to serene environments. Horses relax and spend time together when they are out grazing. You can also reenact this practice by sitting out in the pasture with him while he grazes leisurely beside you. This is similar to two friends chilling together. Match your pace with his, and don't be afraid to talk to him. Let him hear your voice often so he can get used to hearing you and can recognize you. Exercises like this reduce tension between you and are also beneficial health-wise for you both.

Engage in Routine Training

Horses are adventurous creatures who enjoy challenges. Engaging in rigorous and routine training with them helps you develop the bonding process. You need to be careful not to overwork or drain your horses with too much training. Take breaks when necessary and be watchful of the health of your horse. On some other days, you can simply do groundwork maneuvers with your horse. It is necessary to have a balanced training routine, and sometimes, you can add a new activity to challenge your horse.

Groom your Horse Regularly

Grooming is an important way to bond with your horse. Horses in the wild also engage in a similar practice; they groom each other. This is, of course, not done with brushes but by nuzzling their necks against each other. This is a show of affection, and more importantly, they help each scratch those spots they otherwise can't reach on their own.

So, when you groom your horse, you are not only keeping it clean, but you are also scratching parts of his body he will not have been able to reach on his own. Horses have "sweet spots," and regular grooming helps you discover them. Some horses like to scratch while others prefer a gentle touch. Discovering your horse's preference comes in handy when you want to appreciate your horse or help it feel less anxious.

Massage with your Hand

If you have been to a spa or massage, then you know how relaxing massages can be. A good idea for relaxing your horse is by using your hands to softly massage him, preferably in one of the sweet spots you recently discovered. Equine massages are very beneficial and therapeutic for horses, especially when they are feeling nervous or agitated. This also helps to develop a stronger bond because, in time, your horse will associate positive feelings with you. He will look forward to your arrival because your horse knows that when he is with you, he will feel good and relaxed.

Understand the Physical Cues of your Horse

Horse, like humans, engage in non-verbal communication. Since they cannot talk, they express feelings and emotions with non-verbal cues. Often, your horse communicates with you this way, and so as a horse owner, you need to read your horse's body language to know what he is trying to tell you. Their ears, eyes, and tails indicate when the animal is tensed or frightened, happy or relaxed, tired, or ill. There are also times when your horse wants to play, and that is frequently expressed in body language. The more time you spend with your horse, the easier it gets for you to read his body language and attend to his needs.

Explore and Experience Things Together

Sharing an experience with someone has a way of bringing you closer; it's the same with horses. As you explore with your horse, riding or competing, facing different challenges and triumphs, you build a close bond. So, do not fear sharing your emotions with your horse. The bond you can create with your horse can last for a long time.

Respect your Horse's Space

Horses are social animals who thrive when they are together. If you only have one hour, you should allow your horse to mingle and meet with other horses. If you have a herd, create ample time for them to ride and explore together. This will help improve your horse's mood, disposition, and overall health. Horses only have an interest in safety (food and shelter), comfort, and companionship. When you can provide all these for your horse, he will learn to trust and depend on you.

Chapter Five: Housing and Fencing

Before you bring your horse home, you will need to sort out is a place for it to live. Unless you intend to board your horse at a stable, you must have a stable built on your premises. Boarding is a more expensive option, although some people might find it more convenient. You will also miss the pleasure of having your horse around you. Depending on the stable service you choose, you may spend between $200 to $450 per month to keep your horse as a boarding facility. You may even spend more on extra care and training. However, you will free yourself from the stress of daily chores by choosing this option. But what's the fun in that?

If you prefer to have your horse close to you at home, then you must build horse housing and a fence around your property. You will need a lot of space for this. This project will also take some time and, of course, money. Keeping your horse at home also means it will depend on you for daily care, and you will need extensive knowledge of horse care. Eventually, the cost of keeping your horse at home is most likely going to be cheaper than housing it in a stable. So, a house housing and fencing project is a good investment. Still, you will need to plan carefully for shelter, fencing, equipment, storage, bedding, hay, manure disposal, and management of the facility.

Generally, prepare to spend about $1100 annually on the maintenance of a mature horse on your property. This is significantly lower than the cost of boarding. You may spend more if you intend to breed, train, or compete with your horse.

Horse Housing

Building a horse housing facility involves providing everything your horse needs to be safe and comfortable. This includes shelter from the weather and wind, a place to eat, and sleeping facilities. A horse's basic needs differ from those of humans. You have to understand this in planning for your horse housing.

Most times, these basic needs depend on what you intend to do with your horse. If you intend to go for shows, for example, then you will need a place to ride the horse built into your housing facility. But if you are keeping a horse for just casual riding or leisure, then a barn or three-sided shed may be enough.

The truth is that you can spend as much as you want to build a horse housing facility, depending on your budget. You may estimate at least $7 for every square foot of space if you are building an enclosed barn. You may spend even more depending on the bells and whistles you intend to install.

Generally, you need to build an indoor shelter, an outdoor unit, and a walking or grazing area. You will also need one or two storage rooms for food, drugs, and other equine needs. Finally, you will need to install a fence to keep your animal enclosed properly. Let's go over the process of constructing each of these in greater detail.

Indoor Shelter

Your horse needs a place to sleep and rest (typically from 8 pm until 7 am). Generally, each horse will need as much as 16 square meters (or 170 feet) space to stay. This indoor shelter also has to have bedding facilities (usually sawdust), constant access to fresh water and hay, good ventilation, and proper cleaning and maintenance. While designs may vary slightly, this stall will generally have the main door, with an upper half, which opens like a window. This allows you to look into the stall without letting the horse out.

Stall Sizing

The size of your stall depends largely on the size of your horse, among other factors. For a miniature horse, the stall can have a dimension of 6' x 8' per horse. For small horses and ponies that weigh less than 900 lb., a stall with a 10' x 10' dimension is good. You will, of course, need more space for larger horses. A 12' x 12' size is the industry standard. You will need a lot more for a larger draft horse (as much as 16' x 16'). For a stall intended for foaling, you will need a size twice that of a single stall.

Types of Indoor Shelters

Horse stalls can be designed in various ways, depending on your preferences and needs. Some common indoor shelters for horses include the following.

Tie Stalls

This is the most basic type of indoor shelter. In a standing stall, the horse is simply tied forward using a rope or chain. Sometimes, the horse may stand loose with chains across the open ends of the stall. Horses housed this way must have been trained to stand quietly. A tie-stall should be at least 10 feet long and 5 feet wide.

Horse stalls are not very comfortable as they provide very limited space for movement, although they can serve to accommodate in cases where you have limited space available. Tie stalls are less popular these days than they used to be in the past.

Box Stalls

Another option for housing horses is an open-sided or free box stall. This provides a form of protection and shelter for your horse by also allows you to keep it in an open-air area. This type of housing is commonly used to house a group of horses that get along with each other well.

Open Shed Stall

These are similar to box stall but designed in a row with doors that open outdoors. The doors are typically the Dutch-door type with an open top-half for ventilation. Open shed stalls work best in areas with mild-climatic conditions.

Horse Housing Construction Materials

For all stall types, hardwood is the common material used in construction. This hardwood is commonly treated to discourage the horse from chewing the wood. While pine and other softwoods may be used, your horse is most likely going to chew through quickly.

The stall flooring may comprise a crushed rock base, which is typically covered with field lime or clay. Hard surfaces like asphalt or cement may be used for stall flooring. The flooring can also be made of sand. The latter option is less stable and durable than packed lime or clay, although it does allow better drainage and is more comfortable for the horse than harder surfaces that are slippery and hard on a horse's legs.

However, hard flooring is easier to clean than bare sand. You can use hard flooring along with sufficient bedding and some sort of mat, which helps to ease some problems associated with hard flooring options.

Stall Ceiling and Doors

A stall should provide sufficient clearance from the floor. You need a height of at least 10 feet or even higher for good air circulation and safety. Stall doors should be at least four feet wide. *You will need larger doors for a draft horse.*

Generally, you have two options for stall doors. You can either have Dutch doors or sliding doors. If a Dutch door occurs, it should swing open into the aisle and not into the stall. Sliding doors are generally easier to maneuver, but they are generally more expensive.

You must choose between shutting your horse in or having a top window over which the horse can hang its head. Horses not shut in are generally happier, although this also carries the risk of biting passersby.

Doors can be made of a wide range of materials (commonly wood). But steel or wire mesh doors are popular in places with hot climates as this promotes better air circulation. However, the mesh may allow some of the bedding to spill out into the aisle. Generally, your stall horse stall should be well built, rugged, and secure with a "horse-proof" latch with no dangerous or protruding edges.

Bedding

One of the final considerations for indoor housing is the bedding options. Various types of bedding materials can be used, from straw to wood shavings. Which one you go for depends on the availability of material in your area, cost, and suitability for your needs. Straw and wood shavings can be purchased from local lumber manufacturer or furniture makers around you. Other possible options for bedding include rice hulls, sawdust, peanut hulls, paper pulp, and peat moss.

The thickness of the bedding depends, to a large extent, on the flooring. For a dirt floor, be good with just 3 to 4 inches of bedding. For harder floors made with cement or asphalt, the bedding should be at least 8 to 10 inches in depth.

Outdoor Housing

You should be good with a simple three-sided shelter with a sturdy roof. An outdoor shelter houses your horse on hot or rainy days. On average, target a size of at least 170 square feet *per horse* for your outdoor shelter.

The construction cost of an outdoor shelter is generally lower than that of indoor housing. They come in different designs, from three-sided barns to open-ended bars. It is recommended to feed your horse in your outdoor shelter rather than in the barn. This will reduce manure in the barn, and your horses are less likely to fight over food in an open area than they will in a confined space.

The Outside Grazing/Walking Area

Part of your outdoor housing facility is a grazing or walking area. Experts recommend that you allow your horse to graze or walk around for better health and well-being. A space of at least 1,5 acre (6.000 square meters) per horse is recommended for outdoor grazing. There are no strict rules about how this should be designed. However, ensure that you remove foreign objects and rock from this area to avoid injuring your horse.

Feed And Tack Storage

You will also need to consider storage facilities in your barn for hay, commercial feeds, drugs, and other health kits. You need a dry, shadowy room, designed so it keeps your horse feeds fresh and free from pests. The feed storage room should also be out of reach of the horses. How large this will be, and the method of storage depends on how many horses you have to feed. You will also need to plan for a space to store straw and bedding materials.

You will need a special tack room to keep valuable equipment you use on your facility safe and dust-free. You may also add in a few other features to your tack room that makes it more livable like a comfortable chair, storage cupboard, or even a small fridge. Depending on your needs and preferences, you may even go all out with some extra luxury features like a coffeemaker, washer or dryer, microwave oven, and a water heater.

Horse Fencing

Another vital component of horse housing is the fence. In ancient times, those who owned horses were limited to stones and sticks as materials for making fences. Today, thanks to modern technology, modern fences are now made from a wide range of materials. Still, it is impossible to claim one fence type as the only perfect one. Choosing the ideal fencing material involves balancing aesthetics, cost, and safety concerns.

Horse Fence Safety Considerations

Fencing for horses has peculiarities that cannot be ignored. While it is possible to keep pastures of cattle and other farm animals enclosed with a barbed wire fence, this cannot be done with horses.

Fencing for horses is subject to various factors, including the building code of wherever you live. However, there are still major considerations that apply to horse fencing everywhere. For instance, it is generally recommended that horse fencing should be at least 54 to 60 inches high. You may need to make it taller depending on the breed of horses or if your property is next to a highway, or anywhere else that an escape from your premises may be of major concern. Here, a minimum height of 5 feet is recommended for a field fence while at least 6 feet is recommended for stall paddocks and runs.

Experts also recommend that your fence bottom should have an opening of 8 to 12 inches. This opening should be the right dimension to prevent your horse's legs from getting trapped under the fence or foals rolling out. The opening should be wide enough to prevent the hoof from getting trapped or simply too small for the hoof to pass through.

With wire fencing, visibility is one of the major considerations. A wooden fence or one made with PVC material is easily distinguishable for a horse. But wire fences are almost invisible, and in a panic, your horse might run into the fence and risk injury. The visibility of a wire fence can be improved by adding a top rail made of other materials like PVC or wood. Wire fences also tend to be electrified, which helps to create a psychological barrier keeping horses in check.

No matter the type of material used and how it is constructed, present a smooth side of the material to the horse. Also, boards and other fencing materials should be mounted inside and not outside the fence posts, as this makes it more difficult for the horse to knock them loose. Also consider the angle of the fence corners, especially when you have horses that do not get along with each other. With an acute corner angle, a bullied horse is likely to get entrapped. A simple way to solve this is to make the fence corners curved or simply block the corners completely.

Fence Posts

Perhaps the most important part of a fence is the post. This determines the integrity and strength of the fence since the gate and other parts of the fence assembly are braced against it.

Wood Posts

Traditionally, wood is the most commonly used material for making fence posts. The choice of wood in all cases depends largely on the local availability of materials. For instance, in most parts of Western USA, softwood is the most abundant. Similarly, hardwood is more commonly used for fencing posts in the East, Midwest, and Southeast.

Some of the common softwood that may be used for fence posts include redwood, cedar, and cypress. However, they are very expensive, so most people simply go for treated fir or pinewood, which costs less and has been impregnated with chemicals that prevent rust and insect or fungi-damage.

Wooden posts are most commonly driven into the ground. This is a more reliable technique that produces stronger results than digging and back-filling. Wooden posts are commonly used combined with wire materials (like V-mesh wire, high-tensile wire, woven wire, etc.) to reduce the overall cost of the fence. Other materials like vinyl-covered wire products and PVC vinyl-and-wire planks may also be used in combination with wooden posts.

Metal T-Posts

Horse fence posts may also be made from metal materials. These are generally cheaper and easier to install compared to wooden posts. However, metal T-Post offers little in terms of aesthetic appeal.

If you are choosing metal T-posts, make them as safe as possible for your horse. To minimize the risk of having your horse impaled by the pole, top them with plastic caps. The caps to install on your metal T-post should allow the installation of electrified mesh ribbon. This helps to increase the visibility of the fence and prevent socializing or grazing over the fence, which is a common cause of fence damage.

Fence Barriers

The functional part of a horse fence is the barrier, and the quality of the barrier determines how sturdy your fence will be. Ultimately, no barrier is impenetrable, especially if your horse is bent on escaping. However, the goal is to create a fence barrier that is strong enough to keep your horse contained without causing harm to the animal if it charges at the fence. A fence barrier should also serve as a psychological deterrent that helps to keep the horse from escaping. Fence barriers can be made from a wide range of materials, and this includes:

Wood board: Wood is a much-desired material for fencing mainly because of its aesthetics, strength, and enhanced visibility. However, wood is more expensive and high maintenance since they are prone to weathering or horses chewing through them. Spooked horses may also break through wood barriers, and splinters or nails can cause injuries. If you are choosing a wood board barrier, you can expect to spend between $4 to $5 per linear foot of fencing.

PVC board fence: Another visually appealing option for horse fencing is a PVC board. It is just as aesthetically pleasing as wood but without the maintenance headache. But a PVC barrier is even more expensive. You can spend as much as $10 per linear foot of fencing. A PVC material (even when reinforced by internal ribbing) will still break away under pressure. Hence, they are commonly rigged with electricity to keep the animal in check within the enclosure.

Pipe steel: This is an exceptionally strong material for making horse fencing. However, their limitation is also in their strength. Pipe steels rarely give, which means your horse risks serious injury if it runs into this kind of fence. However, since pipe steel fences are highly visible, the risk of this happening is minimal. Pipes are generally cheaper to purchase but difficult to install. Hence labor costs may drive price high since we must hire a professional installer. Modifying this fence barrier will be difficult. Hence, they must be properly planned and installed correctly.

High-tensile wire: This refers to wire under tension, and it is one of the most commonly used materials for fencing barriers. There are different high-tensile wire fencing, which includes smooth wire and woven wire fencing. In these types, the wire is pulled tight against posts and corner assemblies placed intermittently along the lines of the fence to counter the pulling forces.

Hire tensile wire barriers are typically professionally installed since they require the knowledge of various professional techniques that keeps the fence braced properly. Springs and tighteners may also be installed on the fence to ensure that it maintains the right tension despite changes in temperature and stretching.

Smooth wire: This wired fencing is like barbed wire but without the barbs. They are the least expensive wired fencing barrier. The wires are not only cheaper, but they can also span a longer distance and thus can take wide pole spacing of up to 20 feet, which further helps to cut costs. Visibility is a major problem with this wire. To solve this problem, they are typically wrapped in PVC coating that comes in a wide range of colors. It is also recommended that they are rigged with electricity to deter horses from trying to push through or run against them.

Woven field fence: This is another commonly used wire fencing material that finds application in various forms of livestock management. It is inexpensive and effective for keeping horses in check while keeping unwanted wildlife out. Woven field barriers are made from cheap fabrics that have been pot welded or brazed to create a woven effect. The best types use knots at the intersection of the wires. Due to their design, they are more visible than smooth wires, and visibility can be further enhanced by having a top board installed or electrifying the fence.

V-mesh barrier: This is a type of wire fencing material made up of meshes of diagonal and horizontal wires woven to create a diamond or V fabric pattern. Like the woven fence, they not only keep horses in check but also lock out unwanted wildlife and predators effectively. They are thus the top choice for foaling facilities and small paddock enclosures. But they are more expensive with a cost similar to traditional wood fencing.

Electric Fencing

Horse fencing is designed to physically deter horses from escaping and also present a form of psychological barrier that keeps them in check by making them think escaping is too difficult or impossible to achieve. While the fencing materials discussed so far help to achieve the former, an electric fence system provides the psychological deterrent effect.

Electric fencing may be combined with all types of conventional fencing materials, including wood, PVC, and wire fencing. They help to reduce the risk of damage and improve the effectiveness of your barrier. The cost of adding electric fencing to your fence barrier is about 15 cents for every linear foot of fencing.

Typically, an electric fence dispenses a high-voltage but low amperage current. This safely shocks the horse when they lean in, run into, or try to graze over the fence and serves as psychological deterrence. The system typically consists of a charger that dispenses the current, conductive wire materials, and the poles sunk into the ground that completes the circuit. The system must be properly installed and well-maintained to prevent failure in the circuit due to broken wire or poor grounding. Besides professional installation, routine inspection and damage repairs must be carried out regularly to keep the electric system in working condition.

Chapter Six: Horse Nutrition and Feeding

Like all living things, horses eat. This is a no-brainer!!! If you're going to be a conscientious and caring horse owner, it's essential that you become familiar with is horse nutrition and feeding. To stay healthy and strong, your horse must be fed with the right supplement and hay choices needed to maintain good health.

There are several myths and differing opinions about how horses should be fed and what they should be fed with. This makes it all the more difficult to decide on the right nutrition and feeding choices. In this chapter, we will discuss all you need to know about horse nutrition and feeding from the basic nutritional requirements of horses to some of the common guidelines you must be familiar with in meeting those requirements.

Understanding The Digestive System Of a Horse

You need to fully understand horse nutrition and feeding; this means learning about how the digestive system of a horse works. Horses differ from other farm animals and must not be treated the same way in terms of feed.

A horse is an herbivore, but they are hind-gut fermenters rather than multi-gastric non-ruminant animals. This means that they have only one stomach. Horses have a small stomach capacity (usually about 2-4 gallons for an average-sized horse). Because of this small size, the feed your horse can consume at any single time is limited. That they are non-ruminant also affects their feeding habit.

Equids are naturally grazing animals. They may spend as much as 16 hours of the day grazing on pasture grasses. Their stomach can secrete digestive enzymes like pepsin and hydrochloric acid, which breaks down the food in their stomachs. They do not regurgitate food, so overeating is not really an option for horses, and eating something poisonous can be fatal since they cannot vomit whatever they eat.

Another peculiarity about the digestive system of a horse is the absence of a gallbladder. This makes it difficult to digest and utilize foods with high fat content. They only digest about 20% of the fat in their meals, and this can take as much as 3 or 4 weeks to take place. Due to this, normal horse feed is expected only to contain a limited quantity of fat (about 3-4%).

In horses, most nutrients are absorbed in the small intestine, which can hold up to 10 to 24 gallons of food. After the protein, fat, carbohydrates, vitamin, and minerals are absorbed here, most of the liquid portion of the food will be passed on to the cecum where detoxification takes place. This is also responsible for the digestion of soluble carbohydrates and fiber.

This is a general overview of how the digestive system of a horse works. By understanding the peculiarities of these systems, it is easier to understand some of the basic nutritional requirements of horses and how to handle them properly.

Horse Nutritional Requirements

Horses require six main classes of nutrients to survive and maintain good health. These nutrients include water, carbohydrates, fat, vitamins, proteins, and minerals. These nutrients must be combined in the right quantity and proportion for a balanced horse diet.

Water

Water is the most vital nutrients required for a horse's survival. You must maintain a supply of clean water for your horse at all times. On average, they need up to 2 quarts of water with every pound of hay they eat. They will need even more under special conditions like high temperatures, periods of high activity, or hard work, and for lactating mares.

When horses are deprived of water, it may lead to reduced food intake and decreased physical activities. If your horse is passing dry feces or you notice dry mucous membranes in their mouth, they may be dehydrated. Keep a healthy supply of clean water and ensure that the water is palatable and accessible for your horse.

Carbohydrates

The main source of energy in horse nutrition is carbohydrates. The basic building block of carbohydrate is glucose. Starches and sugars are broken down into glucose and absorbed in the small intestine of a horse. The non-soluble carbohydrates are passed into the large intestine, where they are fermented by microbes to release their energy constituent. Most horse feeds contain soluble carbohydrates to varying amounts. Corn is the highest source of carbohydrate or horses. Oats and barley are also great sources, and forages may contain about 8% starch.

Horses need the energy supplied by carbohydrates in order to sustain life. All of your horses' basic functional activities require a supply of energy that is most commonly supplied by soluble carbohydrates and fibers. Signs of energy deficiency in horses include weight loss, low growth rate, low physical activity, low milk production in lactating mares, and so on. Excessive consumption of high energy foods can lead to obesity and increase the risk of conditions like laminitis and colic.

Fat

This is another vital source of energy in a horse's diet. Fat supplies up to 9 MCal of energy per kg of food. This is up to three times higher than what you get when you feed your horse carbohydrates. However, horses have a hard time digesting and absorbing fat. Therefore, only about 2 - 6% fat is contained in pre-mixed horse feeds as higher may be difficult to digest and cause problems eventually.

Protein

This nutrient is crucial for growth and for muscle development in horses. Proteins comprise amino acids and are sourced from food like alfalfa and soybean meal, which are essential parts of a horse's diet. Protein is easily incorporated, and most adult horses need only about 8-10% of the protein in their ration. However, rowing foals and lactating mares may require more than this.

Protein deficiency in horses can lead to weight loss, reduced growth, low milk production, and rough or coarse hair coat. It can also affect the performance of your horse. Excessive consumption of protein can cause electrolyte imbalances and dehydration in horses.

Vitamins

Vitamins are vital parts of a horse maintenance diet. They are in two main categories. The fat-soluble vitamins include vitamins K, E, D, and A. Vitamin C and B-complex are the water-soluble vitamins. Vitamins may be supplied by premixed rations or in fresh green forage. Vitamin supplements may also be given to horses directly during periods of high activity or prolonged stress or when the horses are not eating well due to sickness or any other condition.

The different vitamins can be sourced from various natural sources, especially in green and leafy forages. If your horse is kept in a stall throughout the day, it will need to be given Vitamin D supplement since this nutrient is sunlight is the main source of this nutrient. Vitamin K, B-complex, and C are produced in the horse's body but are also contained in fresh veggies and fruits. These vitamins are not essential requirements in a horse's diet except under conditions like severe stress.

Minerals

This group of nutrients is required for the maintenance of a healthy body structure, nerve conduction, and fluid balance in the cells of the body. Most minerals like calcium, sodium, phosphorus, magnesium, chloride, and sulfur are required in small quantities daily. If your horse is being fed good quality premixed rations or a fresh green pasture, they will get all the supply of minerals they need for health and growth. However, supplementation may be required under special conditions like the restoration of electrolyte balance in horses that sweat excessively – and in young horses.

Horse Feeding Requirements

In this section, we will discuss what to feed horses to get the needed supply of food that meets their nutritional requirement.

Forages

This includes grasses or legumes and makes up a large proportion of a horse's diet. It is difficult to predict the exact nutritional composition of forages since this tends to vary based on the maturity of the grasses, environmental conditions, and the management of the forages. Only a detailed lab analysis can accurately determine the exact nutritional composition of forages. The various types of horse feed in this category are discussed below.

Legumes

Legumes have a high proportion of protein in their composition. They also serve as a good supply of energy and minerals like calcium. To supply the needed nutrients, legumes need optimal growth conditions like good soil and warm weather. The most popular legumes used in feeding horses are alfalfa and clover.

Hay

This refers to forages harvested and dried for later use in feeding horses. It can be in the form of legumes or grasses like orchard grass, bluegrass, timothy, and fescue. Legume hay contains more protein than grass, but they tend to be more expensive. Grass hays have longer leaves and stems than legumes and are most nutritious if they are cut earlier in their growth stage. Although not a sure sign of quality, appearance is one of the main indicators of good nutrition in the hay. This is why you should avoid feeding your horse moldy or dusty hay.

Concentrates

The Association of American Feed Control Officials (AAFCO) defines concentrate feed as one used with another to improve the nutritional balance of the total feed. Typically, a concentrate is intended to be further diluted or mixed to produce a complete feed. While forages/hay is the most common natural source of nutrition for horses, specially formulated concentrates supply specific nutrients like protein, carbohydrates, and vitamins and are intended to be mixed with other feed ingredients based on the recommendation of the manufacturer.

Grains

This makes up another category of ingredients used in feeding horses. Grains can be given alone or mixed with concentrate feed. Some of the most popular grains used in feeding horses are listed in detail below.

Oats: This is arguably the most popular gain used in feeding horses. However, oats are quite expensive. It is typically rich in fiber but has a lower digestible energy value than most of the other grains. Horses also find oats more palatable than most grains and are easily digestible for equids.

Corn: This is another popular grain used in feeding horses. It contains twice as much digestible energy value but is typically low in fiber. You should feed your horses only the right quantity of corn. It is palatable, and given it has a high energy content, it is easy to overfeed corn, which can lead to obesity. You should never feed your horse moldy corn, as this can be lethal.

Sorghum (Milo): This is high energy and low fiber grain for feeding horses. It is typically in a small hard kernel that has to be processed to make it palatable for feeding horses and for efficient digestion. Sorghum is hardly edible as a grain on its own and is most commonly mixed with other grains.

Barley: Barley has moderate energy and fiber content, and it a palatable grain for feeding horses. Like sorghum, it has to undergo some form of processing for easier digestibility.

Wheat: Although wheat is a high energy grain that horses can eat, it rarely is served as feedstuff due to its high cost. It has hard kernels as well and must be processed for easy digestion and must be mixed with other grains to make it palatable.

Supplements

Nutritional supplements are not main feedstuffs. Instead, they are given as an addition or replacement for nutrients that may not be available in sufficient quantity in your horse's regular diet. There are various supplements for horses.

Protein Supplements: The most common protein supplement is soybean meal. It contains high-quality protein and is typically administered to supply essential amino acids. Cottonseed meal and peanut meal are other examples of protein supplements. They contain about 48% and 53% of crude protein, respectively. Brewer's grain (a by-product of the production of beer) is another nutritious and highly palatable protein supplement. Brewer's grain is also commonly used as a fat and vitamin B supplement.

Fat Supplements: Fat supplements can also be added to horse feeds to provide an additional source of fat in horse feeds. Vegetable oil is the most commonly used fat supplement for horse feeding. Rice bran is another ingredient that has become popular in recent times as a feed supplement.

The Rules Of Feeding Your Horse

It is not enough to know what to feed your horse; there are basic rules and considerations for horse feeding to ensure optimum results as far as the nutrition and health of your horse is concerned. Understanding these rules is crucial to your overall knowledge of horse care. Below are some of the most important things to remember when feeding your horse.

Feed your Horse a Lot of Roughage

The bulk of your horse's daily calorie intake should be from roughage. While grain may be given as additional feed for your horse, good quality hay or pasture legumes and grass is just enough and should be the main thing you feed your horse. The digestive system of a horse is best suited for digesting roughage. Always ensure that you have a good supply of roughage available and only serve grains as supplementary feeding.

Generally, a horse will need up between 1 to 2% of its body weight in roughage per day. Grazing horses will typically feed for up to 16 hours of the day. If you keep your horse in a stall for most of the day, you can try to replicate this natural feeding pattern by having hay available in front of them for most of the day. This will maintain a supply of roughage for its digestive system.

Feed Grain Often but in Small Amounts

As earlier explained, grain should not be the main feed for your horses. Instead, you can feed them small amounts of grains multiple times in a day. Small and frequent grain meal replicates the natural feeding pattern of horses better than giving them large quantities of grain at a time. Your horse can digest better this way, and you get much better results.

Change Feed and Feed Schedules Gradually

If you are changing what you feed your horse, you should make such a change gradually rather than switch suddenly. Sudden changes in nutrient supply can cause conditions like founder or colic. The same applies to if you are changing how much feed you give your horse. Increase or decrease your meal food little at a time over a period of several weeks, not suddenly. A simple technique for changing your horse's feed is to replace just 25% of the current feed with the new food every two days. Watch for serious changes and adverse effects so you can make adjustments accordingly.

Feed with an Accurate and Consistent Feed Measurement

One of the most important rules of horse feeding is to ensure that you feed your horse consistently with an accurate measure of feed. Averagely, a thousand-pound equid will need about 15 to 20 pounds of hay daily. Although hay is typically dispensed in flakes, the amount of hay in a flake can vary considerably. It all depends on the kind of hay and the size of the flakes. You should measure the portion of hay you intend to feed your horse and only feed the portion that your horse needs.

Don't Feed your Horse Right Before or After Exercise

Horses are active animals, and they do a lot of physical activities daily. If you have plans to ride your horse, wait for an hour or more after it has finished its meal before you proceed. For even more strenuous activities, a three or four-hour wait is recommended. Also, allow your horse to cool down after work (with the breathing rate fully restored) before feeding. With a full stomach, your horse's lungs (which are essential for all rigorous physical activities) will have less room to expand, and this will make exercise a lot harder for them. Also, during rigorous activities, blood flow will be diverted away from organs in the digestive system, and this can slow down gut movement.

Stick to a Routine

Horses do better when fed on a routine. They have an amazing internal clock that will adjust to feeding time. Therefore, we recommend that you maintain a consistent feeding schedule for your horse at the same time daily. An abrupt change in the feeding schedule can be annoying and may trigger serious health conditions such as colic.

Additional Rules for Horse Feeding

◻ The needs of every horse differ. Hence, consider the size, age, and other peculiarities of your horse in deciding what to feed it with

◻ Consider the hay or pasture balance: if your horse is grazing, with access to good pasture, then you need not feed so much hay anymore. Similarly, horses that don't get enough good pastures will need more hay.

◻ Feed only a minimal amount of grain.

◻ Adjust your horse feed based on the amount of work it does and the level of physical activities.

Chapter Seven: Horse Health and Disease Prevention

Horses are strong animals; however, they are not impenetrable. They can suffer from various types of illnesses or one injury or the other. Even with the best of care, occasional bouts of ill-health cannot be entirely avoided.

Your role as a horse keeper is to reduce the risks and occurrence of these ailments. And even when they do occur, be able to recognize the signs of ill-health in your health and attend to the injuries or disease in time and ensure that your horse receives the treatment it needs.

How To Recognize When Your Horse Needs Care

As a horse owner, recognizing if your horse needs care is an essential skill. Although a horse cannot speak to tell you when it is sick, by knowing the signs to watch out for and carefully observing your horse for these signs, you should be able to identify when your horse is not in good condition and learn the correct ways to care for it. The following are signs that something might be wrong with your horse.

☐ Fever

☐ Irregular breathing and heart rate (too slow or too rapid)

☐ Loss of appetite

☐ Excessive heat in the feet or limbs

☐ Discharge from nose, mouth, or eyes

☐ Swelling on various parts of the body

☐ Sensitivity and exercise intolerance

☐ Colic

☐ Flared nostrils or a frightening appearance

☐ Breathing difficulties

☐ Chronic coughing and unusual sounds

☐ Limping or lameness

☐ Body sores

☐ Constipation and diarrhea

☐ Muscle spasms

These are some signs to look out for. While having these signs does not positively confirm that your horse is sick, it is sufficient reason to invite a vet to take a look at your horse and carry out a comprehensive diagnosis.

Skin Conditions

Ringworm

Ringworm is a type of fungal skin infection that occurs in various animals, including horses. It is so named due to the circular-shaped lesions that occur on the skin. These lesions vary in their density and size and may appear on various parts of the horse's body like the neck, saddle region, neck, or girth regions. Initially, the infection may show as tufts of hair, which eventually fall off and leave behind weeping lesions.

Ringworm is a contagious skin infection that may be spread by direct contact with an infected animal. It may also be spread indirectly since the immediate environment of an infected horse may become infected.

How to prevent and manage ringworm: if you notice a ringworm breakout on your horse, you should isolate the infected animal as much as possible. Items like bedding materials used by the infected horse should also be disposed of. Strict hygiene is important to prevent the spread of ringworms. Also, seek the help of a vet on how to treat the infection.

Rain Scald

This is a skin infection that occurs because of a softening of the skin due to persistent water saturation. It is characterized by patchy hair loss along with the hindquarters and back of your horse. The hair on the site of infection may become matted, and weeping lesions and sores may appear on the spot.

Horses with an already-weakened immune system suffer more from this condition. It may also occur in horses that lack natural lubrication that keeps their coat dry and warm.

Rain scald may also be caused by non-breathable or leaking blankets, which may expose a horse's back to constant moisture.

How to prevent and manage rain scald: keeping moisture away from your horse is the most effective way to prevent rain scald. Ensure that you have a shelter for your horse away from the field and ensure that you used the right type of horse blankets. Keep your horse stall well maintained, clean, and as dry as possible.

Mud Fever and Cracked Heel

Muddy or wet conditions cause this skin condition, characterized by skin inflammation on the legs and stomach of the infected horses. The inflamed area may also be scaly. Severe cases of mud fever can also cause fever or high temperature. Mud fever is a bacterial infection. The bacteria may enter under the skin when it is muddy or waterlogged. Cracked heel is similar to mud fever, as the same factors cause both conditions.

How to prevent and manage mud fever and cracked heel: to prevent this disease, you should clean your horse's legs whenever you bring it in from the field. To get rid of the mud, you can either leave it to dry off before brushing it off or simply wash off the wet mud with water and dry it up. You may also apply a barrier cream, which helps to prevent the horse's skin from getting waterlogged.

Sweet Itch

Also known as Summer Seasonal Recurrent Dermatitis (SSRD), *sweet itch* s a type of allergic reaction characterized by inflammation of the skin. Often, the affected area of the skin may also become itchy. The back, mane, and tail of the horse are the most commonly affected area. A type of midge ("no-see-ums" or gnats) called Culicoides causes it, leading to irritation and an allergic reaction to the saliva of the midge. In serious cases, the horse may rub itself raw against surfaces in other to relive the itch.

Although the appearance of symptoms of this condition depends largely on environmental conditions, a horse that develops this condition as a youngster will suffer from it continually.

The most effective way to prevent sweet itch is to get rid of midges or avoid grazing your horse in areas where they are likely to encounter them. Midges are attracted to areas with a lot of decomposing vegetation, typically in woodlands or areas near the water. Avoid these areas entirely. Avoiding grazing at certain times of the day (midges are more common at dusk or dawn) can also help manage and limit encounters to this insect.

Respiratory Conditions

Common Cold

Horses may suffer from a common cold, characterized by a white or yellowish discharge from your horse's nose. This may also come with a slight fever and swollen glands in the horse's nose. Flu is a viral infection that can be easily spread through contact with an infected person. Horses kept in a poorly ventilated stall for a long period are likely to come down with an infection. If you take your horses on shows, their proximity with other horses may increase the risk of catching a cold.

How to prevent/manage common cold: if your horse comes down with a cold, isolate him from your other animals and call a vet immediately. Keep your horse in a well-ventilated area at all times. Feed infected horses with soft and easy to swallow hay (preferably soaked). When at competitions or public shows, limit your horse's contact with other horses and try to avoid letting the horse drink from public water troughs.

Cough

Various factors can cause coughs. The most common cough is typically associated with the common cold and is characterized by the watery discharge from the horse's nose. This type of cough may span for about two weeks, with the cough gradually increasing in frequency. An allergic reaction is also another likely cause of coughs, as well as bacteria and viruses.

How to treat/manage coughs: if your horse has a cough, get stop the animal from working or any other rigorous activity and get a veterinarian immediately. Treat a viral or bacterial infection if it is the cause. With cough caused by allergic reactions, ensure that your horse's immediate environment is clean and well-ventilated. Bedding and other stable materials should be dust-free, and hay should be soaked in water to limit dust. It is always recommended to keep the horse away from other animals until you have determined the exact cause of the cough.

Other Conditions

Colic

This is a term used to describe abdominal discomfort and pain in horses. Colic is an indication of a problem in the gut or any other abdominal organs. Symptoms of colic include restlessness, pawing at the ground or excessive attempts to roll, labored or rapid breathing, unusual irritability, unsuccessful attempt to pass dung, and elevated pulse rates. Colic can be caused by a wide range of factors, which can be as simple as indigestion or, in more serious cases, a twisted gut. Call in a vet immediately if you notice any sign of discomfort or suspect that your horse may be suffering from abdominal pain.

Laminitis

Also called *founder*, laminitis is an inflammation, weakening, swelling, or even death of soft tissues in the horse's hoof. It is a serious problem that is usually very painful and debilitating. Laminitis is better prevented since it can be difficult to cure. Laminitis can be linked to a wide range of causes, including obesity, insulin resistance, poor nutrition, metabolic syndrome, excessive weight-bearing, cold weather, and serious cases of colic, among others. You may notice an increased amplitude of the digital pulse in the horse's lower limb. This is an early indicator of laminitis. Other signs to watch out for include shifting weight from one foot to the other, inability or reluctance to move, outstretched limbs while standing, and so on. If you notice any of these signs, call for a vet immediately.

Arthritis

Bone arthritis or degenerative joint disease is a fairly common condition that affects horses. It is a common reason horses have to be retired or even put down. Joints affected by arthritis may swell and appear larger than they are supposed to be, which will cause serious pain and make the horse act stiff. Unfortunately, there is really no cure for arthritis. So, it is better to prevent it entirely rather than let it happen. Taking preventive measures as early as possible is the best way to keep arthritis in check. Basic precautions to take include ensuring that your horse always gets sufficient warm-up before any activities, avoiding harmful, hard, and uneven surfaces for riding, and watching your horse's weight, as this may put a lot of pressure on the joints.

Poor Dental Care

Horses may also suffer from dental issues, many of which are commonly associated with poor dental care. A foul odor from your horse's mouth is a clear indication of dental problems. If you notice your horse is behaving abnormally (especially during feeding), their teeth may be the problem. Taking precautions and ensuring proper dental care from an early stage is the best way to prevent dental problems in your horse later on. Schedule annual oral and dental exams for horses older than five years. When left to linger, oral problems can lead to other serious problems for your horse later.

Back Issues

The back of a horse comprises a complicated system of bones, muscles, nerves, and tendons. It is crucial to a horse's comfort, activity, and general well-being. Back issues are one of the major problems frequently encountered by performance horses. If your horse competes often, it is likely to develop back issues. For performing horses, a sudden drop in performance is a likely indicator or back issues. Often, a simple rest for a few days should be able to fix the problem and relieve back pain. In extreme cases, a vet must come in to treat the back problem through mesotherapy or other forms of medical interventions. There are injections, foams, or spray that may be administered to help relax your horse's tired muscles and for a cool and soothing effect. Braces may also be put on your horse to hasten recovery.

Horse Parasites

Horses can be affected by a wide range of parasites. This can be internal parasites like lungworms, ascarids, strongyles, threadworms, tapeworms, and pinworms, or external parasites like ticks, mosquitoes, lice, or horse mange. These parasites are causative organisms or vectors of various common horse diseases. For dealing with horse parasites, prevention and treatment should go hand-in-hand. No horse in the world avoids being plagued by one type of parasite or the other. Regular checks at intervals and seasonal or daily care are needed to keep these parasites in check and prevent various health issues that may be associated with them.

Regular deworming of your horses is one way to deal with various worm parasites. Speak to your veterinarian to help develop a deworming plan for your horse. All the horses on your premises should be dewormed simultaneously and at regular intervals. A single warm specie should be targeted at once for effectiveness, and a correct dosage of dewormer should be used. New arrivals to your premises should be quarantined and dewormed as well before they are allowed to join the other horses on your premises.

Environmental control is an effective way of taking care of insect parasites on your premises. This involves keeping your premises clean and getting rid of conditions that may make it easier for insect parasites to thrive. Targeted insect control and fumigation using insecticides and pesticides may also be carried out to remove specific insect species that may attack your horses. As a horse keeper, be familiar with various insect parasites in your area and learn about how to deal with them effectively and prevent the diseases they spread.

Chapter Eight: Horse Grooming and Daily Care

To keep your horse healthy and strong, regular care is vital. You are not ready to be a horse owner if you are not willing - or you do not have enough time – to carry out the stressful and potentially time-consuming chores of caring for your horse. Horse care chores can be categorized as daily, weekly, monthly, or seasonal care required to keep your horse healthy and happy. Falling behind or failing to carry out any of these tasks can make your horse stall unsafe and unsanitary for horses, leading to a wide range of health problems.

Basic Daily Tasks

Some of the basic daily tasks that should be carried out by a horse owner include:

☐ Feeding: Ideally, your horse should be fed on a forage-based diet at least twice or more throughout the day with the right type of feed and accurately measured quantity. See the previous chapter for guidelines on proper feeding practices.

☐ Watering: Your horse should always have a healthy supply of water available. Horses need about 10 gallons of water per day in warm weather. More or less may be required depending on the activity and general weather conditions.

▢ Cleaning: Regular cleaning of horse stalls, including removing wet or soiled bedding from the stall and getting rid of manure piles from paddock areas.

▢ Exercise: Horses are high-activity animals. They need at least 30 minutes of exercise daily.

Keep an eye out for your horse and look out for any signs of injury and illness so it can be identified and treated immediately.

Weekly Tasks

These tasks should be carried out at least once per week or multiple times in a week based on your schedule and the specific needs of your horse

▢ Bathing and grooming the mane, tail, hooves, and other parts of your horse's body

▢ Cleaning the water trough or buckets

▢ Several hours of exercise or workout

▢ Maintenance clipping

Other Periodic Tasks

Other important tasks should be scheduled and carried out periodically either at a specific season, after a certain period of time, or as your horse requires them. These general preventive care steps help prevent a wide range of preventable conditions and diseases. These include:

▢ Pest control and routine control of internal and external parasites

▢ Vaccination

▢ Dental checks and general oral care

▢ Maintenance and checks of horse shelter and fencing

⬜ Power-washing stall walls and floor

These are a few activities that must be carried out to keep your facility running and maintain the health and wellbeing of your horses. While these might seem like a lot of chores, most horse owners find these activities enjoyable – even therapeutic. If the work required is less than the time you have on your hands, you may consider hiring extra hands to assist you. Do not raise horses if you don't have plans for handling these responsibilities.

Horse Grooming

Grooming involves a series of activities aimed at taking care of the coat, hooves, and the hair of your horse. It provides an opportunity to bond with your horse. Grooming also allows you to look closely and check your horse for injuries or signs of irritation. Hence, it is a chore that must be performed regularly. Ideally, groom your horse daily. However, even if daily grooming is impossible, you should at least spend some time grooming your horse before riding. Taking time to groom your horse will help get rid of grit n your horse's back. Having grit underneath the saddle will be quite uncomfortable for your horse and will lead to sores.

Grooming Tools

There are several tools you will need for horse grooming. You should always have them available and arranged in a convenient shelter. Some tools and materials you will need for horse grooming include:

⬜ Curry comb

⬜ Body brush (with stiff bristles)

⬜ Tail or mane comb (plastic is preferable to metal)

⬜ Finishing brush (should be soft and fine)

⬜ Clippers or scissors (not compulsory)

⬜ Hoof pick

⬜ A soft cloth or clean sponge

⬜ Grooming spray (not compulsory)

⬜ Hoof ointment (not compulsory, but may be recommended by your farrier)

You can gather all of your grooming tools in a wide bucket or buy a grooming box to keep them all organized.

Instructions For Grooming

Before you groom, tie your horse safely and securely using a quick-release knot or cross ties. Below is a basic guide for grooming your horse.

How To Clean Your Horse's Hooves

Begin by sliding your hand down your horse's left foreleg and squeeze the back of the leg just along the tendons. Instruct your horse to raise its legs up by saying "hoof," "up," or whatever word your horse responds to. When your horse raises its hoof, raise it up and pry away any grit, dirt, or manure that may be lodged in the sole (or frog) of the horse's foot. While doing this, also check for injury, grease heel, or thrush. Pay attention to cracks in the hoof and consult a farrier if you notice any problem. Once you are done cleaning and inspecting the hoof of the left foreleg, you can repeat the same for the remaining three legs.

How to Curry Your Horse

The next task will be to curry your horse. Beginning from the left side (offside) of your horse, gently use your grooming mitt or curry comb to loosen and remove any dirt on the horse's coat. Currying also helps to remove any grit, mud, and other debris. Gently curry the horse's coat with circular sweeps over the horse's body. Be extra careful when currying bony areas of your horse's hips, shoulders, and legs. Also, be careful when brushing the belly and back legs of your horse. Some horses are sensitive to this and may react violently to rigorous brushing. If you notice that your horse is swishing his tail in an agitated way or he lays back his ears, then the brushing is probably too rigorous.

Currying is an opportunity to inspect the skin of your horse for signs of injury, wounds, and skin lesions. Watch out for these as you carefully curry your horse's coat, and if you notice any, check the injury and decide if it is something you can treat on your own, or you must invite the vet.

How to Comb-Out Tangles

Combing your horse's tangles helps to give your horse a flowing and shiny mane and give it a full and healthy look. To comb the mane, begin with a mane brush or comb and brush at the bottom of the mane strands. Brush downwards until the mane is untangled, and you can smoothly comb the mane from top to bottom.

Be careful when you do this and position yourself correctly. For safety, stand to one side of your horse then pull the tail gently to your side. This way, you stand completely clear should your horse decide to kick. Having a grooming spray as part of your grooming collection is a good idea. This helps to detangle the hair effectively and makes brushing out the strands of mane a lot easier.

Using the Body Brush

When you are finished brushing, use the body brush to get rid of dirt on your horse's body. A body brush is a stiff brush with loner bristles that will help to get rid of dirt and grit you missed with your curry comb. Begin from one side of your horse in gently sweeping strokes toward the hair growth. The curry brush is generally considered more effective for cleaning parts of the body like the legs than the curry comb. While using the body brush on your horse, check for signs of skin irritation and lesions on the knees and legs. Also, watch out for small nicks and cut and assess the severity of the injuries.

Using the Finishing Brush

The finishing brush has softer and softer bristles and helps make your horse's coat smooth and shiny. Most people also use a finishing brush to clean their horse's face if they do not have a brush specifically for that.

With the finishing brush, gently remove dust that might have been missed by the body brush. Gently use this brush to remove dust from areas like the horse's throat, face, or ears that were most likely missed by the other brushes. The fine and soft bristles of the finishing brush will help smooth the hair and leave your horse with a glossy and shiny coat.

When finished, you can apply a grooming spray. This is not compulsory, but it can help to shine your horse's coat and may also serve as a form of sun protection. Some grooming sprays can make the horse's hair slippery. Avoid using products like this in the saddle area, especially if you intend to ride soon.

Cleaning the Ears, Muzzle, Eyes, and Dock Area

When finished with the rest of your horse's body, it is time for more detailed cleaning. Using a soft cloth or a soft damp sponge, gently wipe clean the area around the eyes and muzzle of your horse to get rid of any dirt that may be present. Doing this also allows you to observe your horse's eyes closely and check for signs of injury or infection. Look out for symptoms like redness, swelling, or excessive tearing.

Do this for the ears, but be careful. Some horses are fussy about having their ears handled. Be careful not to pinch or pull the hairs when you clean it. With time and special care, your horse may come to love having its ears groomed.

Chapter Nine: Horse Breeding

If you raise horses, one of the main things you will need to be familiar with is horse reproduction. While some parts of the reproduction process depend on the attending veterinarian, the efficiency of a horse breeding operation depends largely on your understanding and management of the process.

Horse reproduction aims to produce healthy foals after each successful mating. There is an elaborate process leading up to foaling, and the success of the breeding stage depends on your understanding of your mare and stallion's reproductive performance. In this chapter, we will discuss some essentials of horse breeding and reproduction you are expected to be familiar with as a horse owner. While you can simply have a vet handle or advice you on some of the reproduction processes, it will be better if you also have some of the information necessary for successful horse breeding. This will help you make the right decisions and get the best results.

Horse Selection

One of the most crucial aspects of horse breeding is choosing a horse for breeding. Usually, this is one of the major factors that will determine the success of the breeding process. The probability of getting a healthy and strong foal is also subject to your horse selection process.

It pays to have the progeny information of your horses, as this will help to identify the superior breeding stock. Your vet can assist you with selecting a healthy stallion and mare for breeding. When this is done right, the breeding process is likely to yield better results leading to a successful pregnancy and a healthy foal.

The Reproductive Examination of the Mare

A reproductive examination is necessary to ascertain the reproductive state of your mare. This process involves rectal palpation and ultrasound examination. In a reproductive examination, the mare's vagina, cervix, and vestibule are examined by your vet to determine if they are in a good reproductive state.

Reproductive exams are better done in a stall or the stall entrance rather than in an open field. This helps to keep the horse restricted and also provides some degree of protection to the vet and other personnel handling the horse. If your mare has a foal, they should be not be separated as this will only make the mare agitated and make the examination difficult. Besides having the horse properly restrained, it will also be helpful to have one more person available to assist the vet.

To prevent the spread of disease from one mare to another, disposable equipment should be used. The mare should be washed to get rid of fecal material and dirt from the vulva before examination. With an ultrasound examination, it is best done indoors, away from sunlight, so the vet can easily read the screen of the ultrasound machine.

Understanding the Mare's Estrous Cycle of the Mare

Like all animals, a mare goes through a monthly fertility cycle in response to fluctuations in hormone production. This reproductive cycle is completed in about 21 days. In horses, the reproductive cycle takes place in two phases. There is a continuous cycle during which the mare is in heat (or in season), typically lasting about 5 to 7 days. There is also the dioestrus cycle, which is the period in-between successive heat periods, lasting for about 14 to 16 days).

In non-pregnant mares, the estrous cycle is typically stimulated by increasing daylight. Hence it coincides with the early spring season. There is usually a transitional phase that may persist for a few weeks and might be characterized by short irregular cycles. However, after the first ovulation period, the estrous cycle will become more balanced and regular until autumn, when the mare will enter into an anoestrous cycle again, and ovulation stops.

Hormonal changes in the mare cause the estrous cycle. The hormones produced during the various stages of the estrous cycle include progesterone, prostaglandin (PG), luteinizing hormone, estrogen, and follicle-stimulating hormone (FSH). The production of these hormones determines the progression of the estrous cycle, and some are necessary for the maintenance of pregnancy.

Mare Management

Breeding in horses is relatively inefficient compared to breeding in other domesticated animals. Generally, about an average of 50 percent of mares sent to a stud ever get to produce a foal. This is a hugely inefficient and wasteful process. One factor that probably affects the success rate of horse breeding is a poor selection process of mares for breeding. As a horse breeder, you must identify some of the possible reasons and factors that contribute to wastage in horse breeding and work around them.

An effective mare fertility assessment is important for successful breeding. This practice is used to determine if a mare is suitable for service. Fertility assessment will also help to identify the factors that may contribute to reduced fertility. It will rate mares and place them in order of priority based on the probability of the success of the breeding process.

Proper fertility assessment will also ensure that a mare is served only when it is an estrous period, as this gives it a better chance of conception. At the end of every breeding season, detailed veterinary inspection and a series of examinations should be performed for your mares. Mares that fail to conceive should be assessed and problems identified and rectified before the start of the next breeding season.

Stallion Management

Managing a stallion depends largely on the purpose for which it is being raised. Stallions can be raised for show, racing, or for breeding. This will determine how the stallion will be managed in terms of handling, exercise, health care, and of course, fertility assessment.

If you are raising your stallion for breeding, then a basic understanding of the reproductive system is required. A stallion reproductive system consists of the scrotum, testes, penis, the accessory glands, epididymis, and spermatic cord. These organs must be in a healthy condition for a stallion that is being raised for breeding.

Horse Teasing

One of the essential stages of horse breeding is the teasing process. It will be nearly impossible for your mare to conceive if you do not have an efficient teasing program. The effectiveness of this process depends largely on how well you can determine if the mare is in heat and will be receptive to stallion service. Typically, once the breeding season starts, you have a narrow window of 5 to 7 days within a 21-day monthly cycle. The remaining 14 to 16 days of the estrous cycle are off days during which conception is unlikely.

Although some mares will show signs they are in an "on" season in the absence of a male horse, most mares must be stimulated by a stallion or colt before they show they are on heat. Teasing can be done in various ways. However, no matter how it is done, you must have a flexible and systematic approach since each mare is unique, and the same approach cannot work for all mares.

Some signs that are mare is an estrous period include:

 Accepting the teaser

 Lifting of the tail

 Urinating

 Winking

 Squatting

If a mare is not estrous, it will show the following signs:

 Rejection of the teaser

 Kicking the teaser

 Pulling back the ears

 Clamping her tail down

Interfering in the Horse Breeding Process

Sometimes, human intervention may be required to achieve some control and improve the chances of success of a horse breeding program. This can be in the form of hormone therapy and artificial lighting programs.

Hormone Therapy

Hormone production is one of the critical factors that influence the horse breeding process. Hormone therapy is usually carried out as a way of manipulating barren or maiden mares to improve their chances of conception. Foaling mares may also undergo hormone therapy.

When done correctly, hormone therapy can improve the reproductive performance of your mare quite significantly.

Record Keeping

Another essential aspect of a horse breeding program is record keeping. Keeping a complete and comprehensive record of your horses will play a major role in helping you make educated decisions about the chances of a breeding attempt. Aside from the progeny record of the individual stud and mare, you also need to keep a teasing record on all your mares and have it available to your vet during a mare fertility assessment.

Artificial Lighting Programs

Light plays a significant role in the estrous cycle of horses. The onset of the breeding season is typically determined by longer periods of sunlight. Therefore, a properly implemented artificial lighting program can improve the performance of mares since the breeding cycle is influenced by periods of daylight. By increasing the length of daylight using artificial light, mares can be encouraged to come into season earlier than they will normally do. Artificial lighting can also help improve productivity in foaling mares.

Laboratory Aids to Improve Reproductive Performance

Besides simple fertility assessments and tests, several laboratory tests may be carried out to understand fertility in your horses, diagnose problems, and deal with medical issues. Some tests that may be carried out include bacteriological examinations, biopsy, cytology, hormone assays, and endoscopic examinations.

Serving the Mare

Now that you understand the basic principles of horse breeding and the factors that determine the success of a breeding exercise, you can now proceed with the mating of the horses. Remember that the success of this stage depends on the efficiency of your selection process and the horse teasing itself. The four major ways of getting your mare to foal include hand service, paddock mating, artificial insemination, and embryo transfer.

Chapter Ten: Foaling and Weaning

Once a mare has been successfully impregnated, the pregnancy lasts for approximately 330 to 342 days. You must understand how to accurately diagnose pregnancy early, as this will ensure that you do not return a pregnant mare for servicing. Pregnancy can be diagnosed manually, using an ultrasonic examination, or by a laboratory test.

A pregnant mare requires good quality care, as this can significantly influence if the pregnancy will be carried to term and the health of the foal produced. Basic care for an expectant mare includes:

▢ Provision of nutritious forage

▢ Reduce exposure to other horses to reduce the risk of injury and disease

▢ Vaccination and deworming

▢ Additional care by a veterinarian

▢ Do not transport your mare during pregnancy unless it is absolutely necessary.

Twin conception is typically problematic for mares. This is one reason why early pregnancy detection is important. An ultrasound exam should be carried out a about 14 to 16 days post ovulation, and one of the embryos should be eliminated to allow the other to develop normally.

Signs Of An Impending Birth

Typically, pregnancy will last for about 330 to 342 days. A birth approaches, there are some signs to watch for that indicates that a birth is imminent. While the time-frame of these signs varies from one mare to the other, prepare for an impending birth. Some of the most obvious and reliable signs to look out for include:

 Filling of the udder (occurs at about 2 to 4 weeks pre-foaling)

 Distension of teats (this occurs about 4 to 6-day pre-foaling)

 Waxing of the teats (occurs 1 to 4 days pre-foaling)

 Obvious dripping of milk

 Increase in calcium content of milk (this can be detected with a stall-side test kit)

Other less obvious signs include relaxation of the vulva, changes in the position of the foal, and softening of the croup muscles.

It is difficult to pinpoint an exact day of foaling. However, during the final stage of pregnancy, the mare will begin to show some signs of labor. The signs to watch out for at the onset of labor include:

 Restlessness

 Getting up and down

 Curling of the top-lip

 Weight shifting and picking up the hind legs

 Frequent urination & defecation

 Tail swishing

Foaling

When a mare is ready to foal, it will be advantageous to have an attendant present. Usually, the mare will get only a little or no assistance. But it will still be beneficial to have someone at hand to offer assistance if needed.

During birth, the chorioallantois ruptures, and the foal begins to move through the pelvic canal. The foal should present with two forelegs with its nose resting in-between them. Uteri and abdominal contractions will push it out, and this should take about 10 to 20 minutes.

Usually, the mare should be able to have its foal without assistance. If assistance is to be given, then it has to be in the form of gently holding the feet of the foal and letting the mare push on its own. The attention of a vet should be *required* only in cases of abnormal presentation of the foal.

Care of the Newborn Foal

Within 30 minutes of its birth, a healthy foal should be able to stand on its feet after some failed attempts. Once steady, it will seek out the mare's teats to nurse. This is somewhat random, but with gentle assistance from the mare, the foal will eventually find the teat and suckle on instinct.

Following below are the expected behaviors within the first two hours of a foal's birth:

☐ Foal breathes (immediately after birth)

☐ Lifts its head (within five minutes)

☐ Attempt to rise within 10 minutes and successfully does so within 55 minutes.

☐ Vocalize (within 45 minutes)

☐ Defecates (within 30 minutes)

☐ Suckles (Within an hour)

⬜ Starts walking or running (within 90 minutes)

⬜ Take a nap (within 3 hours)

Understanding normal foal behavior is essential to diagnosing possible problems and seeking help if you need it.

Within the first few weeks of its birth, the foal will nurse quite frequently at an estimated range of one or two 3-minutes sessions within an hour. With time, the duration and frequency of suckling will decrease, and they eat other feedstuffs more. The foal will remain close to its dam for the first few weeks but will gradually explore its immediate environment further.

Right after the delivery of a foal, the first thing to do is to ensure that the foal is breathing. Approach the foaling area quietly to check if the foal is breathing and remove the birth sack from the foal's head if you need to. Once you have confirmed that the foal is breathing, your work is done for the moment. Leave the foaling area and only observe from a distance.

However, if the foal is not breathing on its own immediately, you can tickle its nostrils using a piece of straw or grass or blow into its mouth. If these do not work, shake and rub the foal vigorously, squeeze its ribs gently, or lifting it off the ground slightly and dropping.

Do not cut the umbilical cord immediately after birth. Rather, wait for the mare or foal to break it off as they move. Once the cord breaks, add 1 to 2% mild iodine to the stump to dry it and prevent a bacterial infection, which can lead to severe illness or even death in foals. Continue to observe this naval stump for a few days to ensure that it closes, and if it doesn't, call in a vet.

Usually, the foal should be able to stand on its own within an hour of its birth. The first few attempts may be unsuccessful, but with time, the foal will get the hang of it and should become steady after a while. Let the foal stand by itself, as lifting it onto its feet before it is ready can lead to a strain the tendons and ligaments.

The foal should instinctively search for the udder within an hour of its birth. Again, this is an exploratory process that might take a while for the foal to get used to. Resist the urge to intervene as this can affect the bonding between the mare and the foal. An intervention will be required only if the foal has not nursed within two hours of its birth – or if you notice that the mare is rejecting the foal's attempt to nurse.

Gently help the foal stand on its feet and guide it towards the udder. Sometimes, a mare with a swollen udder or a young and inexperienced mare with sensitive teats must be restrained before she willingly allows the foal to nurse. In extreme cases, the mare may have to be tranquilized by a vet if it continually rejects the foal's attempt to nurse.

Colostrum

The first form of fluid produced by the mare immediately after the birth of the foal is known as *colostrum*. This milk contains antibodies for disease protection and other essential nutrients. Hence, it is vital that your foal receives colostrum soon after it is born. The foal's ability to absorb these essential antibodies will reduce drastically after 12 hours of birth. Ensure that you get your foal to nurse from the mother within this time.

You can increase the number of antibodies present in the mare's colostrum by vaccinating it about 30 days before foaling. If this is not done, then you have to give the foal a tetanus shot at birth. This will help protect the foal for about two to three weeks while its umbilical stump heals.

Colostrum also has laxative effects, and it will help the foal to pass fetal excrement (also known as meconium) shortly after taking it (usually within four hours). Constipation may occur if the foal cannot defecate within the stipulated time.

Common Foal Health Problems

Diarrhea: this is an uncommon problem in foals and may indicate a more serious underlying condition. Severe cases of squirting diarrhea can cause dehydration, weakness, or even death of a newborn foal. Older foals (about one to two weeks old) may experience mild cases of diarrhea. Foal heat scours may also cause diarrhea. This is caused by a parasite known as Strongyloides westeri, which may be transmitted from an infected dam to a foal through breast milk. For a healthy foal, a mild case of foal heat course rarely causes serious harm. However, if you notice that the foal is dehydrated or weak, then you should call in a veterinarian immediately.

Limb weakness & deformities: foals can be born with deformities in the limbs like crooked legs, knuckling, weak pasterns, and general limb weakness. While most of these conditions are likely to correct as the goal grows, you can call in a vet to have it checked just to be sure and recommended treatment if any is required.

Hernias: hernias are defects in the body wall, which leads to the extrusion of part of the horse's intestine under its skin. This defect can occur around the scrotal area or naval of the horse. Mild cases of hernia are self-corrective; surgery may be required in severe cases.

Entropion: this refers to a condition where the foal is born with its eyelids and lashes turned out the wrong way. This can cause tearing or irritation. Often, it is possible to roll the effected eyelid with your hands. But sometimes, special eye treatment may be needed to correct the defect.

Jaundice Foal

Jaundice is a rare condition caused by an incompatibility in the mare and foal's blood group leading to a formation of antibodies in the mare's breast milk. When the foal nurses, these antibodies can be passed to their bodies, and this can have debilitating effects – and may even be fatal without prompt treatment. Call a vet for help immediately if you suspect the foal might have jaundice. Also, discontinue nursing from its mother's milk until treatment is administered.

Caring for Orphaned Foals

In the unfortunate event of a mare's death after foaling (or due to maternal rejection), a foal may require extra care from you. Orphaned foals can still be raised successfully when you know what to do. Absent a mother, one of the first things to do is to ensure that you get the foal colostrum soon after its birth. You may be able to purchase frozen colostrum from a large breeding farm or vet near you. Thaw the frozen milk (do not heat or microwave) and feed your foal with it. A vet can also administer oral colostrum or carry out plasma transfusion as a replacement for regular colostrum.

The easiest way to care for an orphaned mare is to transfer it to a nursing mare. But you must disguise the mare using any strong-smelling liquid like whiskey, milk, urine, or linseed oil. You may also have to restrain or tranquilize the adopted nursing mare until she willingly accepts the orphaned foal. An alternative is to allow the foal nurse on goat milk, although it will be difficult to find goats than can produce enough milk to meet the nutritional needs of a foal. Bottle-feeding or bucket-feeding the foal is the next best alternative if the other options are not available. You can find nutritionally balanced mare replacer milk at feed stores and feed it to your foal.

If you bottle-feed or bucket feed an orphaned foal, try to introduce it to other horses soon so it can learn normal equine behavior and it does not become attached to you. You can place your orphaned foal next to a gentle gelding or mere in a pen if the older horse can be trusted not to hurt the foal.

Before we look at how to wean a foal, here is a checklist of the things you need to do right after the birth:

1. Ensure that the foal is breathing

2. Put iodine on the umbilical cord stump

3. Ensure that the foal gets colostrum as soon as possible

4. Give the foal a tetanus shot if colostrum is not available right away

5. Ensure that the foal passes meconium and treat diarrhea if any

6. Check the umbilical stump to ensure it closes

7. Continually check the foal for several days for signs of infection and call a veterinarian immediately, if necessary.

Horse Weaning

In the first few months of its life, a foal will spend most of its life close to its mother and will depend fully on the mare for its food. By the end of the third month, only about 60% of its time will be spent with the mare. Milk production in the dam will typically continue until the dam is about five to seven months old. At this point, 70% of the foal's nutrients will come from non-milk sources. At this stage (at about five months), you should begin plan to wean your horse. Here is a checklist of things to do to:

1. Gradually increase the foal's feed ration over a period of two to three weeks.

2. Although the dam's milk will start to lose its nutritional value at about three months, you can further reduce milk production by reducing the mare's feed ration.

3. Watch your foal closely during the weaning period. Do not wean the foal if it is ill or isn't thriving well, if it is still attached to its mother, or not eating enough of the feed ration.

4. Your foal has to be halter-broken for a successful weaning.

Weaning a foal can be done gradually or abruptly, depending on factors like the mare's temperament, facilities you have available, and the presence of other horses.

Chapter Eleven: Basic Horse Training

One of the most interesting aspects of horse raising is horse training. It can be challenging, especially for a beginner. Horse training (especially for young horses) is best left in the hands of experienced trainers since young horses tend to be unpredictable, and you need the right skills and experience to handle them.

This training requires time and patience, and it is also about bonding with your horse; still, it is a rewarding experience. As you train your horse to do something new, you also learn something too. It's not all of that cowboy-style horse breaking that you see in old wild west movies!

Basic horse training is about teaching your horse to be ridden the *right way*, and it is not as dangerous as typically portrayed. It cannot be rushed; neither can you train your horse all the skills it needs to learn all at once. Below, you'll find the simple steps of basic horse training.

Take Time To Build a Bond

The first – and perhaps most important – step of basic horse training: taking time to build a bond with your horse. If a horse is not comfortable around you or does not trust you enough, it will be difficult, if not impossible, to teach it anything. You need to give your horse time to get used to you for effective communication between both of you. Building a bond with your horse involves spending time with the horse, creating a positive association, and learning how it communicates with you.

Spend More Time with your Horse

To develop a solid bond with your horse and train it effectively, you must spend more time with it. Horses learn better by routine and repetition. The more time you spend on bonding, the more likely the horse will get comfortable around you. You spend more time with your horse when you groom, bath, or braid their mane. You can also hand-walk your horse around your property.

Creating Positive Associations

To train your horse, you have to teach your horse to associate your presence with positivity. If your horse is always agitated in your presence, you cannot teach it anything. At the start of training, begin with low-stress and pleasurable activities. Doing this will help the horse associate your presence with a sense of calmness. Maintaining a positive attitude and rewarding your horse when it gets the smallest things right will help associate training with positivity.

Most horse trainers subconsciously switch into training mode when they are instinctively demanding for too much from their horse. When you do this, you not only stress the horse, but you are also not allowing the horse to enjoy your presence. The focus should be on building a relationship with the horse rather than merely training it to do your bidding. Both you and your horse will become frustrated if you do this.

Learn How Your Horse Communicates

Taking time to bond with your horse will help you learn more about your horse and how it communicates. This is not about telling your horse *what to do*. As you communicate with your horse, it will communicate back, and you must learn to watch out for these cues.

Every horse is unique, so even as an experienced horse trainer, you will learn new things when you train a new horse.

Learning about your horse involves their likes and dislikes, what it fears, and what encourages it to learn better. Doing this will help you learn how to handle your horse the right way.

How long this entire process will take (of getting used to your horse) depends on various factors. Your commitment to training and the horse's personality will affect how fast you can build a bond and get started with riding and training your horse.

Horse Training Groundwork

The very foundation of any horse training routine is groundwork. This basically refers to the art of training your horse *on the ground.* There is a popular saying among horse enthusiasts that "Whatever you cannot get your horse to do on the ground, it will not be able to do it with you in the saddle."

Horse training groundwork involves several simple training and exercises which include:

⬜ Training your horse to stand still

⬜ Flexing

⬜ Properly leading your horse

⬜ Softening

⬜ Getting your horse to move in a circle

⬜ Basic motion (hind-end and shoulder movements)

Although it might be tempting to skip this step and move straight to saddle training, this is not recommended. Groundwork is the first place to start to introduce new training to your horse.

Standing Still

One of the basic things you have to train your horse to do is stand still. When you train your horse to stand still, it can pay attention to you as its training and look to you for the next instruction.

How to: Have the horse on a halter and lead, then stand facing the horse while holding the lead rope. Allow the lead to slack and stand still. Shake the lead rope each time the horse steps out of its original position. If the horse does not back up immediately, shake the rope harder until it gets the message and responds. With continuous training, your horse should learn to back up when you shake the rope as it realizes that walking off is wrong.

Properly Leading

While leading a horse is a fairly simple task, a horse not trained will have some trouble with leading. Leading your horse properly will help establish that you are the one in charge. You will need a halter lead rope for this exercise. A lunge whip will also be necessary.

How to: The correct position to lead your horse is at your elbow. The horse should walk behind you on the side where you are leading it. If the horse is falling behind, you can encourage it to maintain pace by simply waving the lunge whip at it behind you. If the horse is being pushy and is trying to walk ahead of you, stop immediately and get the horse to back up. Repeat this as many times as possible until the horse learns to respond correctly.

Flexing

A horse flexes when it bends its neck to either side. This exercise trains your horse to respond when pressure is applied at the reins. At the end of the flexing training, your horse should turn its neck so that its nose touches its right or left shoulders.

How to: Hold the lead rope and bring your hand to the horse's withers. Apply some pressure on the rope. Your horse should bend its neck towards the source of the pressure. And even when it does, you may need more time and training to get it to bend its neck all the way until you no longer feel pressure on the lead rope. Hold the pressure continuously until the horse eventually dips its nose further, and the pressure on the rope is released. Reward your horse once this is completed. Repeat the exercise for the other side.

Softening

The goal of this drill is to get your horse to lower its head when you apply pressure to its lead rope. This will help your horse to accept a bit more conveniently later. It will also train your horse to respond to pressure on the bit.

How to: For this drill, grab the base of the horse's lead rope, and apply some pressure to pull it down towards the ground. Your horse should respond by lowering its head. If it does not do this right away, maintain steady pressure on the rope and release it as soon as the horses dip its head even slightly.

Desensitizing Your Horse

Asides groundwork, another aspect of training your horse is desensitizing it. This involves getting your horse used to certain things it is not normally used to. Throughout its lifetime, your horse must get familiar with otherwise unfamiliar things like having a saddle on its back or having someone sitting in its saddle. An untrained horse will react strangely. Desensitizing helps to build trust in your horse and prepare it for pressure and some form of discomfort, so it does not react strangely in certain situations.

Desensitizing your Horse to a Saddle

There are a lot of things you have to desensitize your horse to, but top on the list is saddling. Without training, the first instinct of your horse when you place a saddle on it will be to flee. Saddle training will make your animal more trusting and better prepared for saddling for the first time.

The goal of this exercise is to prepare your horse to have things placed on their back, around their stomach, or touching their sides.

To desensitize your horse to saddles, you will need a saddle pad, tarps, or plastic bags.

One way you can prepare your horse is by rubbing these materials all over the horse's body. This will help prepare your horse for when the tack is actually placed on it. When you rub your horse with these materials, if it attempts to move away, simply stop and hold the material on its body until it stops moving.

You will also have to desensitize the horse to pressure. A saddle will apply pressure to the sides and back of the horse. You should start getting the horse used to this pressure before you actually start riding it. Other parts of the horse's body where gear will be worn like the legs and face, should be desensitized to pressure. Let your horse get used to having a bridle and bit, so the horse gets familiar with what it feels like.

Putting the Saddle On

Once your horse has been trained and desensitized, you can put the saddle on. Remember that putting the saddle on is still a new experience, so your horse can still get frustrated and react unpredictably. Saddle training your horse helps it become comfortable having a saddle on its back.

Repetition is one of the most effective ways to get your horse used to saddling. Practice putting the saddle on and pulling it off repeatedly. Repeat this as often as you need to leave the saddle on for longer each time. With time, you should be able to let the horse move around the pen with the stirrups at its side for a while before pulling it off again.

Practice throwing the saddle over the back of your horse from both sides. This will ensure that the horse gets completely comfortable with having the saddle thrown from either side.

The most challenging part of getting your horse familiar with the saddle is attaching the girth. Once your horse shows it is comfortable with having the saddle on its back, you can now gently attach the girth to the saddle on one of its sides. But don't leave it hanging on the side as this can make the horse nervous.

To avoid this, attach the girth on one side then gradually rub the other end of the girth over the horse's belly and legs. Swing the girth back and forth under the horse's belly until it feels comfortable. You can then proceed to the other side of the horse and pull the girth and tighten it properly. Once you have been able to do this, undo the girth and allow it to fall to the side of the horse again. Repeat this action until your horse gets used to it. Some people just tighten the girth and let their horse buck around to wear itself out. *This is not good practice.*

Desensitizing your Horse to Having Weight on the Saddle

Once your horse has gotten comfortable with having a saddle on its back, the next step is to get it accustomed to having weight added. This will prepare your horse for an eventual ride – which is the ultimate goal.

You cannot simply proceed to sit on the back of an untrained horse. You need to patiently get him used to having weight on its back. Once you have the saddle on the back of your horse, you can begin weight desensitization by putting your arm gently over the back of your horse to mimic the feeling of having weight on its back.

You can also try jumping up beside the horse like you are about to mount up, but you do not mount yet. Do this gently, and in a relaxed and playful way, so your horse does not feel threatened and take off. Next, you can try laying across the back of your horse on your belly. This position is great since it also allows you to get off the horse fast if you need to.

Now you can sit on your horse. But do this carefully. As a precaution, turn your horse's nose towards you as you try to mount, so it doesn't freak out on you. To start, place one foot on the stirrup and put some of your weight on it without swinging your leg over the horse's back yet. If your horse seems calm about this, then proceed to stand in the stirrup. Wait for your horse to adjust before finally swinging your leg over to sit in the saddle.

You should sit for a few seconds, then dismount. Do this repeatedly while gradually increasing the time so you don't overwhelm your horse. Finally, when your horse is comfortable with you having you sit in the saddle, you have to train it to get familiar with the application pressure under the saddle (which is crucial to riding it) further. This is the stage where you will see the full benefits of good groundwork. You will also have to train your horse to get familiar with various types of movement in the saddle, so it doesn't freak out with any slight movement.

Be Patient and Reward the Smallest Tries

Throughout the entire process of training your horse, be patient. You don't want to rush your horse through the processes. Throughout your training, reward your horse for even the slightest tries, especially when you begin riding. You want your horse to associate an action with a positive reward.

Do not put too much pressure on your horse or ask for too much, especially if the horse is newly-trained. The horse might have a hard time understanding what you are trying to do. But if it shows any positive sign, rewarding it will let it learn that that was the correct response. Training a horse is simple and fun. You have to understand only your horse's actions and reactions and figure out how to use his training effectively. If you are new to horse training, you can either get someone else to train your horse or have a professional trainer you can call for help every step of the way.

Chapter Twelve: Training Athletic and Show Horses

Horses are kept for a wide range of reasons. For most horses, basic training is enough. But if you are raising your horses for special purposes like racing or shows, then your horse will need additional training. We cannot fully cover all horse training in this book, but this chapter will run you through the basics of horse training for athletic purposes and shows.

Horse Training for Races

Before you train and condition your horse as a racing prospect, you should first evaluate it objectively. This involves both physical evaluations of the horse's gait and structure and psychological evaluations of its attitude. Is your horse well-built enough to handle the stress of moving at a great speed? Will your sweet colt, easily pushed out of the way by other horses, have the drive to become a top racehorse? There is no sure way to tell, but an objective observation and evaluation will guide you in choosing the horse to train.

Once you have carefully evaluated your choice of the horse to train, you can condition your horse for racing. There are multiple factors to consider as far as training racehorses is considered. This includes respiratory conditioning (aerobic and anaerobic conditioning) and physical conditioning - or fitness training.

Aerobic Conditioning

Horses depend on both aerobic and anaerobic respiration during rigorous physical activity. Aerobic respiration refers to regular respiration in a resting state or during low energy activities. As the rigor of physical activity increases, the horse will switch from aerobic to anaerobic breathing. The importance of aerobic conditioning is to delay how long your horse can depend on aerobic respiration before it needs to switch to anaerobic energy sources. Aerobic conditioning also helps to shorten recovery time after a race or workout.

The main exercise involved in aerobic conditioning is slow, long-distance work. This is an ideal way to begin aerobic conditioning for your horse or whip it back into shape after a long period away from training. Aerobic exercises basically consist of walking and trotting routines, and some cantering exercises.

In aerobic training, the horse may be galloped for a few minutes, then allowed to recover by walking or trotting. The longer the workout, the longer the recovery time required. The amount of bouts the horse will take per day depends on the horse's response and your desired progression.

During aerobic workouts, track the heart rate of your horse; you may do this manually or simply use a heart rate monitor for this. The normal resting heart rate of usually about 40 beats per minute. While walking or trotting, the heart rate may be raised to about 80 to 140. A heartbeat rate between 150 to 160 per minute (or less) should be targeted.

Depending on factors like age, condition, and response rate, this initial period of aerobic conditioning may last for about six to eight weeks or more before you switch to intense exercises and race training. With horses being trained for shows, skill work is introduced after the period of aerobic conditioning has been completed.

Anaerobic Conditioning

Horses rely on both anaerobic respiration and aerobic respiration for high-powered activities like racing. Horses will typically switch from aerobic to anaerobic energy consumption when their heart rate exceeds about 150 beats per minute.

Sprinting or breezing exercises are required to improve the anaerobic capacity of your horse. These exercises also work to improve bone structure and strength. Anaerobic conditioning for horses can be executed in two ways. You can increase the speed of the horse over a short distance or increase the workout distance it has to cover and gradually push for more speed.

Horses should not be pushed for maximum speed capacity during a workout. In fact, your horse simply needs to go at about 70 to 80% of its maximum speed during all workouts; the same is true for race distance. This is important to avoid overwhelming and overworking your horse.

Most trainers follow an "interval training" plan. This involves working out two days in a week with the horse making multiple short sprints on each day with rest periods of rest in-between those sprints. The horse is expected to reach a maximum heart rate of 200 to 250 per minute during this training.

A sprinting horse should be observed closely and evaluated for signs of respiratory distress, bone or muscle soreness or other problems, and workout should be discontinued to allow the horse to recover if any of these are observed.

Pay Attention to Your Horse's Weight and Diet

During these respiration training routines, you must evaluate the physical condition of your horse. An overweight horse must lose weight during its workout, and you must focus on routines that make this possible. Similarly, if your horse is underweight, you must increase its food ration, especially with fatty foods. However, the fat should be introduced slowly to avoid adverse effects on your horse's digestion. The diet of a horse in training should also contain minerals, and vitamins, and access to clean and fresh water at all times.

Horse Training for Shows

If you are training for shows, your horse needs to learn specific tricks. Many showmanship competitions are for showcasing the ability of a handler to perform skills with the horse. However, no matter the handler's skill, only a well-trained horse can perform the intricate moves that win shows.

Showmanship training also offers additional benefits, even outside the show ring. Basic show training will improve the horse's manners and respect. It will also improve its ability to maintain control over its pace and position. Some skills may also be useful for real-life scenarios.

Basic Horse Training for Shows

There are six major maneuvers involve basic showmanship training. You can teach your horse these basic maneuvers, and these techniques can be combined in different ways and serve as the basic foundation for more advanced techniques.

▢ Leading at a walk

▢ Backing up

▢ Leading at a jog

▢ Pivoting

▢ Stopping

▢ Setting up

Before we describe these maneuvers in greater detail, you must understand basic things about training your horse to perform these skills. To train these maneuvers, you apply pressure on a lead chain. You also direct your horse with pressure from your own body sometimes. Reward every correct response by releasing pressure and pausing briefly before you give your horse the command for another maneuver.

Some exaggerated body movements or verbal cues may be required in training, especially for beginners. However, as your horse progresses, you must refine or adjust these cues until they are virtually non-existent or subtle as these cues and train your horse to adapt and follow instructions without them.

Note that progress in horse training is slow and steady. Your horse may not produce the results you want right way, but consider any close approximation to what you want as a desired response and reward accordingly.

Leading at a Walk

Goal: This drill is aimed at training your horse how to lead calmly at the same pace as you are moving while maintaining its body on a straight line.

How to: The starting position of this drill is such that the offside of your horse is positioned close to a fence or guardrail to align its motion. The trainer should be positioned between the middle part of the horse's neck and its throatlatch. Start off on a quick walk without moving your arms. Incline your shoulders in a forward direction to serve as a visual command for a forward motion for your horse. Also, apply some pressure on the chain to get the horse to follow you as you move.

Leading at a Jog

Goal: This exercise trains your horse to step into a trot or jog when you start running, all while keeping its body straight.

How to: The starting position of this drill is the same as the previous ones. Start with a walk with your elbow positioned on your side and your lead-hand anchored. With your body tilted forward, step forward and break into a small jog or run. Keep your elbow and lead hand steady as you run. If the horse responds accordingly and can adjust its pace to yours, relieve some of the pressure on the chain. You can also return to a brief walk after some seconds of jogging or trotting. If it does not break into a jog as expected, you may need to use verbal cues.

Stopping

Goal: The goal of this training is to get your horse stopped in a balanced and soft manner and with its body straight and properly aligned.

How to: Maintain the same starting position as the previous training and start with a walk. As your horse walks with you, give a stop command softly, such as "whoa." Stand still immediately as you give this command. This verbal cue will help your horse associate the command with the action. At first, your horse may go past you a bit but will stop moving when the rope tightens against its chin. After a while, your horse should be able to respond to the stop command. When it does, reward accordingly by releasing the rope pressure. Repeat the command as many times as possible until your horse is used to it. With time, you should be able to eliminate the verbal cue entirely.

Backing

Goal: This training is aimed at getting your horse to back up smoothly and calmly and with its body aligned properly when a command is given.

How to: Begin this training in the lead position earlier described. Turn your body to the opposite direction (now you should be facing the rear end of the horse). Align yourself with your arm or shoulder level with the muzzle of the horse. While still holding the lead rope, take one step forward (use your left leg first) and apply a rearward pressure on the chain. With this motion, you should be invading your horse's space. This training is to get your horse to step back when you do this. Usually, the horse will only move one of its legs out of the way. With time, it should adjust fully and back up properly with both legs.

Setting Up

Goal: The goal of this exercise is to train your horse to set itself up with its legs under him. Your horse will learn to maintain this position until you give it another command.

How to: These techniques can be taught in various ways, so the method we will describe here is just one of the many ways it can be done. Start this training in the standstill position earlier described, then turn to face the horse. In this position, be positioned on the left side of your horse's head. Hold the lead chain close to the juncture of the chain and leather parts.

The first step is to control the movement of your horse's feet. Begin by making the horse move its left hind leg close to the right hind leg. You can control the horse to push its foot forward or backward, depending on the initial position of the right leg relative to the left. Pull-on the chain until you get your horse to respond appropriately. Reward a correct response with a pressure release.

Pivoting

Goal: This training is aimed at getting your horse to anchor itself on the spot on its right hind-foot. The horse will then pivot around that foot by crossing its left leg across the right one.

How to: Begin by facing the left side of your horse and position yourself just across the throatlatch. With your left hand, hold the shank at the point where the chain and the leather meets. To initiate movement, apply a light forward pressure to the chain and step forward step with your right leg. This will encourage your horse to step his left front leg in front of the right. Raise your hand slightly to tap the horse on its left shoulder. This cue and body language should make the horse move its legs and shoulders in the right direction. Take the training one step a time until your horse can complete a 360-degree full pivot.

Beyond these basics, your horse must learn more advanced maneuvers that cannot be covered in this book, especially if you intend to go fully into showmanship. However, this is a good basic foundation to start with. You can find additional materials at a feed or tack store, or contact a professional trainer for help.

Conclusion

Raising horses is no easy job, which is why many people choose boarding facilities instead. If you raise your horses on your own land, then you have to be ready to commit and put in the required work. This includes preparing housing facilities, proper nutrition, health, grooming, and daily care for your equine friend.

Raising horses also requires an in-depth knowledge of horse breeding, foaling, and weaning. Depending on your purpose for raising horses, you must learn about training your horse. This includes basic horse training and advanced training for athletics or showmanship.

Horse raising is a highly beneficial venture. Horses serve many purposes, including simply human companionship, helping you make the best use of your free time, and as work animals on farming facilities. Keeping horses can also be beneficial for your health.

You may also raise horses for commercial purposes or train your horse for equestrian sports. No matter your reason for raising horses, this book summarizes all the things you need to know about breeding healthy and strong horses. I hope you have learned enough in this book to set you on the right path on your journey to becoming an expert hostler.

Here's another book by Dion Rosser that you might like

Made in the USA
Monee, IL
30 May 2024

59126244R00066